CURRICULUM AND EVALUATION
S T A N D A R D S
FOR SCHOOL MATHEMATICS
ADDENDA SERIES, GRADES 5–8

GEOMETRY IN THE MIDDLE GRADES

Dorothy Geddes

with

Juliana Bove

Irene Fortunato

David J. Fuys

Jessica Morgenstern

Rosamond Welchman-Tischler

Frances R. Curcio, Series Editor

Consultants

Diana Lambdin Kroll

Frank K. Lester, Jr.

Kenneth P. Goldberg

NC
TM
NATIONAL COUNCIL OF
TEACHERS OF MATHEMATICS

Copyright © 1992 by
THE NATIONAL COUNCIL OF TEACHERS OF MATHEMATICS, INC.
1906 Association Drive, Reston, Virginia 22091-1593

Library of Congress Cataloging-in-Publication Data

Geddes, Dorothy.
    Geometry in the middle grades / Dorothy Geddes with Juliana Bove
  . . . [et al.] ; consultants, Diana Lambdin Kroll, Frank K. Lester,
 Jr., Kenneth P. Goldberg.
        p.   cm. — (Curriculum and evaluation standards for school
 mathematics addenda series.   Grades 5–8)
    Includes bibliographical references.
    ISBN 0-87353-323-2
    1. Geometry—Study and teaching (Elementary)   I. Bove, Juliana.
 II. Title.   III. Series.
 QA461.G43 1992
 372.7—dc20   92-15551
                                                                  CIP

Printed in the United States of America

TABLE OF CONTENTS

FOREWORD

In March 1989, the National Council of Teachers of Mathematics officially released the *Curriculum and Evaluation Standards for School Mathematics* (NCTM 1989). The document provides a vision and a framework for strengthening the mathematics curriculum in kindergarten to grade 12 in North American schools. Evaluation, an integral part of planning for and implementing instruction, is an important feature of the document. Also presented is a contrast between traditional rote methods of teaching, which have proved to be unsuccessful, and recommendations for improving instruction supported by current educational research.

As the *Curriculum and Evaluation Standards* was being developed, it became apparent that a plethora of examples would be needed to illustrate how the vision could be realistically implemented in the K–12 classroom. A Task Force on the Addenda to the *Curriculum and Evaluation Standards for School Mathematics*, chaired by Thomas Rowan and composed of Joan Duea, Christian Hirsch, Marie Jernigan, and Richard Lodholz, was appointed by Shirley Frye, then NCTM president. The Task Force's recommendations on the scope and nature of the supporting publications were submitted in the fall of 1988 to the Educational Materials Committee, which subsequently framed the Addenda Project for NCTM Board approval. Following the release of the *Curriculum and Evaluation Standards* and on the basis of recommendations of the NCTM Task Force (Rowan 1988), writing teams were assigned to develop addenda to provide teachers with classroom ideas for translating the *Standards* into classroom practice. Three writing teams were formed to prepare materials for grades K–6 (Miriam A. Leiva, editor), grades 5–8 (Frances R. Curcio, editor), and grades 9–12 (Christian R. Hirsch, editor).

The themes of problem solving, reasoning, communication, connections, technology, and evaluation have been woven throughout the materials. The writing teams included K–12 classroom teachers, supervisors, and university mathematics educators. The materials have been field tested in an effort to make them "teacher friendly."

Implementing the *Curriculum and Evaluation Standards* will take time. The Addenda Series was written to help teachers as they undertake this task. Furthermore, the Addenda Series is appropriate for use in inservice staff development as well as for use in preservice courses in teacher education programs.

On behalf of the National Council of Teachers of Mathematics, I would like to thank all the authors, consultants, and editors who gave willingly of their time, effort, and expertise in developing these exemplary materials. In particular, I would like to acknowledge gratefully the work of Dorothy Geddes and her contributing authors, Juliana Bove, Irene Fortunato, David Fuys, Jessica Morgenstern, and Rosamond Welchman-Tischler, for preparing *Geometry in the Middle Grades*. Special thanks are extended to Diana Lambdin Kroll and Frank K. Lester, Jr., evaluation consultants, and Kenneth P. Goldberg, technology consultant, for their contributions to the entire Grades 5–8 Addenda Series. Finally, this project would not have materialized without the outstanding technical support supplied by Cynthia Rosso and the NCTM staff.

Bonnie H. Litwiller, Addenda Project Coordinator

PREFACE

The purpose of *Geometry in the Middle Grades,* as well as of the other books in the Grades 5–8 Addenda Series, is to provide teachers with ideas and materials to support the implementation of the *Curriculum and Evaluation Standards for School Mathematics* (NCTM 1989). In addition to this book, the other publications in this series are *Understanding Rational Numbers and Proportions* (Bezuk, forthcoming), *Measurement in the Middle Grades* (Geddes, forthcoming), *Patterns and Functions* (Phillips 1991), *Developing Number Sense in the Middle Grades* (Reys 1991), and *Dealing with Data and Chance* (Zawojewski 1991). These books are *not* an outline of a middle school curriculum, but rather they present several topics and activities to exemplify the ideas advocated in the *Curriculum and Evaluation Standards,* and they provide examples to help students make the transition from elementary to high school mathematics.

The unifying themes of the *Curriculum and Evaluation Standards,* the characteristics of a new classroom learning environment, and the role of evaluation are described below. The discussion in each of these parts will refer to examples in this book.

Unifying Themes

The unifying themes of the *Curriculum and Evaluation Standards* include mathematics as problem solving, mathematics as communication, mathematical reasoning, and mathematical connections. These themes are not separate, isolated entities, but rather they are all interrelated. The ideas, examples, illustrations, and activities presented in this book are designed to demonstrate the interrelationships by weaving these themes throughout the activities as well as by providing ideas for incorporating technology and evaluation techniques.

Mathematics as problem solving. Although problem solving has been a goal of mathematics instruction throughout the years, it became the focus of attention with the advent of NCTM's *An Agenda for Action* (NCTM 1980). The *Curriculum and Evaluation Standards* reaffirms the importance of problem solving in mathematics instruction.

The excitement of learning and applying mathematics is generated when problems develop within the context of a situation familiar to students. Allowing them to formulate problems as they naturally arise within the context of everyday experiences gives them the opportunity to put mathematics to work, observing its usefulness and its applicability (e.g., Activity 2b). However, "not all problems require a real-world setting. Indeed, middle school students often are intrigued by story settings or those arising from mathematics itself" (NCTM 1989, p. 77). For example, see Activity 13a.

Mathematics as communication. Although the formal language of mathematics is concise, is high in concept density, and may be seemingly foreign, students should have the opportunity to bring meaning to mathematics on the basis of their experiences. Allowing them to talk about their experiences and how they relate to mathematics concepts, listen to each other as they share ideas, read mathematics in various formats (e.g., number sentences, graphs, charts), and write about mathematical situations affords students the opportunity to compare experiences, clarify their thinking, and develop an understanding of how the mathematics they study in school is related to the mathematics they experience in the "real world." This requires the integration of the four language arts—speaking, listening, reading, and writing—with the mathematics lesson (e.g., Activity 10).

Communicating in mathematics requires a common language and familiarity with modes of representing mathematical ideas. Depending on students' "comfort level," oral language, prose, manipulatives, pictures, diagrams, charts, graphs, or symbols can be used to communicate ideas (e.g., Activity 2). Students should be encouraged to translate from one mode to another. Spatial visualization skills are developed in many activities (e.g., Activities 1, 2, 6, 14, 16).

Mathematics as reasoning. During the middle school years, students should have opportunities to develop and employ their abilities in logical and spatial reasoning as well as in proportional and graphical reasoning. The development of a student's reasoning ability occurs over a period of time. We can observe extreme differences between students in grade 5 and students in grade 8. As a result, instructional approaches must reflect these differences. The van Hiele model of thinking is a focus of many activities in this book (e.g., Activities 8, 9, 11, 13).

Depending on students' readiness, exploratory activities, experiments, and projects may require them to give a descriptive account of what they observe, an informal argument based on empirical results, or a formal proof supporting a conjecture (Hirsch and Lappan 1989). Active learners should be constantly involved in questioning, examining, conjecturing, and experimenting (e.g., Activity 11).

Mathematical connections. Traditionally, mathematics has often been presented as an isolated set of rules to be memorized. The *Curriculum and Evaluation Standards* suggests that mathematics be presented as an integrated whole. Students should observe the interrelatedness among branches of mathematics: number theory, geometry, algebra, probability, and so on (e.g., Activity 5). Furthermore, students should become aware of how mathematics is related to other disciplines such as science, art, literature, music, social studies, business, and industrial technology (e.g., Activity 22).

There is no guarantee that allowing students to explore, create, and experiment within the context of a problem-solving setting will lead them to discover connections between and among mathematics concepts. Teachers may need to guide students in discovering connections and to elicit these connections explicitly. Students who recognize connections within mathematics and with other disciplines can understand and appreciate the logical unity and the power of mathematics (Steen 1989).

A New Classroom Environment

Implementing the *Curriculum and Evaluation Standards* requires a new way of teaching. The traditional teacher roles of authority figure and information disseminator must change to learning facilitator and instructional decision maker.

Knowledge about students and how they learn mathematics can contribute to establishing a conducive learning environment for middle school students. The teacher selects the instructional objectives on the basis of knowledge of his or her students, knowledge of mathematics, and knowledge of pedagogy (NCTM 1991). After selecting the instructional objectives, the teacher must decide how to deliver the content. Is the use of manipulatives appropriate? Is the use of technology appropriate? Is a cooperative learning setting appropriate?

Appropriate use of manipulatives. Manipulatives are multisensory tools for learning that provide students with a means of communicating ideas by allowing them to model or represent their ideas concretely. Using manipulatives, however, does not guarantee the understanding of a mathematics concept (Baroody 1989). After allowing students to explore using manipulatives, teachers must formulate questions to elicit the important, "big" mathematical ideas that enable students to make connections between the mathematics and the manipulatives used to represent the concept(s) (e.g., Activity 5d).

Appropriate use of technology. Developments in technology have made the traditional, computation-dominated mathematics curriculum obsolete. As a result, technology has been given a prominent place in the *Curriculum and Evaluation Standards*, in terms of which technology should be made available for use in the classroom and how technology should be used in mathematics instruction. It is expected that at the middle school level, students will have access to appropriate calculators, and computers should be available for demonstration purposes as well as for individual and group work (NCTM 1989, p. 8). It should be noted that new advances in technology are being made constantly. Teachers should keep abreast of new developments that support mathematics instruction.

In this book, suggestions are made for integrating the use of computers to study relationships between and among geometric shapes (e.g., Activity 4b), to test and examine conjectures (e.g., Activity 13d), and to explore and investigate problem situations (e.g., Activity 12). Specifically, Logo and the Geometric PreSupposer are used in several activities.

Appropriate use of cooperative learning groups. Traditionally, mathematics has been taught as a "solo," isolated activity, yet in business and industry, mathematicians often work in teams to solve problems and attain common objectives (Steen 1989). Allowing students to work in cooperative groups affords them the opportunity to develop social and communication skills while working with peers of various ethnic, religious, and racial groups.

Cooperative learning environments, characterized by students working together and interacting with each other, contribute to internalizing concepts by forcing the students to defend their views against challenges brought by their peers. The value of this approach is supported by the work of Vygotsky ([1934]1986), who discussed the increasingly interrelated nature of language and cognition as children grow.

Cooperative groups usually contain three to five students and may be established for various lengths of time (Artzt and Newman 1990; Davidson 1989). Unlike most traditional small-group instruction in reading and mathematics, cooperative learning groups are heterogeneous, and everyone must work together for the common good of all. Students who understand the concept being discussed are responsible for explaining it to those who do not understand. Examples for using cooperative learning can be found in Activities 7, 10, and 14. When using cooperative groups, teachers must consider new ways of evaluating performance to ensure the success of the instructional objective(s).

The Role of Evaluation

Making changes in the content and methods of mathematics instruction will also require making changes in why and how students' work is evaluated. Evaluation should be an integral part of instruction, not limited to grading and testing. According to Kroll and Lester (1991), there are at least four reasons for collecting evaluation information:

- ♦ To make decisions about the content and methods of mathematics instruction
- ♦ To make decisions about classroom climate
- ♦ To help in communicating what is important
- ♦ To assign grades

In other words, evaluation includes much more than marking right and wrong answers. It "must be more than testing; it must be a continuous, dynamic, and often informal process" (NCTM 1989, p. 203). What methods can be used for evaluation purposes? The *Curriculum and Evaluation Standards* recommends that teachers use a variety of types of evaluation. Kroll and Lester (1991) discuss four major categories of evaluation: (1) *observing and questioning students*, (2) *using assessment data reported by students*, (3) *assessing students' written mathematics work*, and (4) *using multiple-choice or short-answer tests*. Teachers might, for example, observe and question students to assess their understanding and to gain insight into their feelings and their beliefs about mathematics; use holistic scoring techniques for a focused assessment of students' written problem-solving work; or collect information through students' responses to short-answer questionnaires or through written assignments such as journal entries or brief essays. Using these multiple methods of collecting assessment data will contribute to a thorough evaluation of students' work. These and other evaluation techniques are discussed in more detail in Kroll and Lester. This book contains an evaluation section following the teaching notes in each of the four clusters of activities. Evaluation ideas include the use of such alternative techniques as portfolios, "journal writes," and laboratory reports.

This brief description of the unifying themes of the *Curriculum and Evaluation Standards*, the characteristics of a new learning environment, and the role of evaluation is furnished as a starting point to understand and to appreciate the ideas that are presented in this book. It is hoped that these ideas provide a foundation for developing concepts in geometry in the middle grades and generate interest among teachers for improving instructional and evaluation techniques in mathematics.

Frances R. Curcio, Editor
Grades 5–8 Addenda Series

INTRODUCTION

Informal geometry and spatial thinking are vital aspects of the mathematics curriculum for the middle grades. Modeling, mapping, and engaging in activities and spatial experiences organized around physical models can help students discover, visualize, and represent concepts and properties of geometric figures in the physical world. When given opportunities to create plans, build models, draw, sort, classify, and engage in geometric fantasies and mathematical creativity through problem solving, middle school students will experience the fun and the challenge of learning geometry. Through geometry explorations and investigations, students develop spatial intuitions and an understanding of geometric concepts necessary to function effectively in a three-dimensional world.

Geometry is grasping space ... that space in which the child lives, breathes, and moves. The space that the child must learn to know, explore, conquer in order to live, breathe, and move better in it. (Freudenthal 1973, p. 403)

The study of geometry not only can provide an avenue for divergent thinking and creative problem solving but also can develop students' logical thinking abilities. A challenge to the visual thinking of students and adults alike is the following pictorial puzzle (fig. 1).

On a trip to a city surrounded by many waterways, a series of photographs of some historical landmarks (a lighthouse, a water tower, and a steeple) was taken from the deck of a cruising ferryboat. Unfortunately, the resulting pictures were dropped and got mixed up. Can you find in which order the pictures were taken? The map is a view of the waterway region.

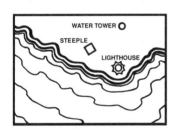
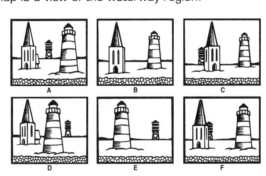

Fig. 1

Geometric concepts and representations contribute effectively to learning number ideas. In *Everybody Counts,* the National Research Council states: "Geometry ... [is] as important as numbers in achieving mathematical power" (1989, p. 43). Geometry has been identified as one of the twelve components of essential mathematics for the twenty-first century by the National Council of Supervisors of Mathematics (1989). From geometry experiences, students gain insights that strengthen their understanding of other areas of mathematics.

So important are geometry and spatial sense in the mathematics curricula that the National Council of Teachers of Mathematics (NCTM) in recent years has published entire issues of the *Mathematics Teacher* (September 1985, geometry focus) and the *Arithmetic Teacher* (February 1990, spatial sense focus) on these topics; also, the 1987 Yearbook of the NCTM was devoted to a comprehensive study of *Learning and Teaching Geometry, K–12* (NCTM 1987).

Geometry is included in the mathematics curriculum recommended for grades 5–8 in the *Curriculum and Evaluation Standards for School Mathematics* (NCTM 1989). In addition, geometry and spatial perception are topics particularly well suited for focus when addressing the four standards common to all grades K–12, which were described in the Preface: Mathematics as Problem Solving, Mathematics as Communication, Mathematics as Reasoning, and Mathematical Connections.

Purpose of This Book

Inductive reasoning involves looking at a collection of particular cases for emerging patterns. For example: Given the sequence of numbers 2, 4, 6, 8, 10, _?_, _?_, the next two numbers might be 12 and 14.

This book will address issues and concerns about teaching and learning geometry and spatial thinking in relation to implementing these standards. The book is not a geometry curriculum for grades 5–8. Rather, it presents different approaches to some geometry topics and provides a collection of sample activities organized into four sections: Two- and Three-Dimensional Geometry Concepts; Relationships among Properties of Shapes Including Angle Sums; Transformation Geometry; and Enrichment Topics. An investigative approach is used to encourage students to discover patterns and make conjectures. The examples and activities are designed to develop students' intuitive sense of geometry concepts, to foster higher-order thinking, and to help students value the essential role of geometry and reasoning in our society. *Geometry in the Middle Grades* considers the teacher's role in creating classroom settings (that is, managing small groups, encouraging cooperative learning, and using manipulatives) that foster and require a dynamic interaction of students with their environment.

Deductive reasoning involves making inferences from a given set of premises. For example: All cows have four legs. Elsie is a cow. Inference—Elsie has four legs.

Students' experiences in learning geometry should make them perceive geometry as having a dynamically important role in their environment and not as merely learning vocabulary, memorizing definitions and formulas, and stating properties of shapes. The *Curriculum and Evaluation Standards* envisions a classroom learning environment in which middle school students, working in groups or independently, explore and investigate problem situations in two and three dimensions, make and test conjectures, construct and use models, materials, manipulatives, and available technology, develop spatial skills, use inductive and deductive reasoning, and then communicate their conclusions with conviction and confidence. Students should be continually challenged to consider alternative approaches and solutions and "what if" extensions in their problem explorations.

Implementing the Curriculum and Evaluation Standards: Illustrative Examples

Geometry is a branch of mathematics rich in visual approaches to problem exploration, pattern finding, and reasoning in the middle grades. A few illustrations are given below to show how the *Standards* can be implemented, with several of the goals being addressed simultaneously. Consider this problem:

> Friends are invited to a party. At the first doorbell ring, one guest arrives; at the second ring, two more guests than on the first ring arrive; at the third ring, two more guests than on the second ring arrive; and so on. How many guests are at the party after the fifth ring? The eighth ring? The tenth ring? The *n*th ring?

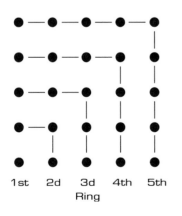

1st 2d 3d 4th 5th
Ring

Fig. 2

Some students may solve this problem by acting it out, examining a simple case, or looking for patterns. A "dot" representation (fig. 2) of the problem provides still another approach to the solution. The follow-up class discussion of this geometric representation of square numbers should be extended to include consideration of the visual representations of oblong, triangular, and other figurate numbers (see Activity 5a). An examination of the relationships among these numbers leads to interesting pattern finding and the formulation of conjectures. For a related discussion, see Phillips (1991).

Another example of how a problem can be given a geometric representation follows. Students explore and find strategies for solving the well-known "handshake" problem (How many handshakes will occur at a party if every one of the twelve guests shakes hands with each of the others?). After the students have solved this problem and extended it by considering the number of handshakes for twenty guests, fifty guests, and so on, pose these problems:

Fig. 3

Draw twelve distinct points on the circumference of a circle. Connect each point by a line segment to every other point. How many line segments are drawn? (See fig. 3.)

How many diagonals are there in a polygon of twelve sides? Extension: If the polygon has twenty sides (fifty sides, *n* sides), how many diagonals will there be? (See fig. 4.)

Fig. 4

Class discussion and student explorations of these problems (with student comments such as, "Oh, this is like the handshake problem") furnish opportunities for students to discover connections between seemingly unrelated problems.

Problems that allow for student explorations with materials and manipulatives are especially appealing to middle grade students. To develop concepts and to encourage creative explorations, it is essential that students use tangrams, geoboards, centicubes, Miras or Reflectas (fig. 5), mirrors, grids, two- and three-dimensional models, construction devices, D-Stix, and geostrips. Middle grade students enjoy making collapsible and other three-dimensional models, and these constructions help develop spatial thinking and visualization (see Activity 2). Using geoboards affords many opportunities for students to explore relationships, discover patterns, make and test conjectures (including the Pythagorean theorem), and engage in cooperative learning (see Activity 14).

Mira   Reflecta

Fig. 5

Problems in real-world settings also provide students with opportunities to see connections among mathematical ideas and real-world applications. For example, students working in small groups can investigate tessellations and their applications to tiling, fabric design, art, and manufacturers' packaging decisions (see Activity 10). Cooperative group activities such as the above give students opportunities to use language in communicating mathematical ideas, to explain, to use inductive reasoning, and to engage in divergent thinking.

In concept development, it is important to have students examine examples and nonexamples of the concept, compare and contrast these examples, and give other instances and noninstances of the concept before they are asked to develop a written or verbal definition or description (see Activities 2, 3, and 4). After a brief experience with "concept cards," students become quite skillful in creating concept card assignments for their peers.

Written as well as oral communication is essential for mathematics learning, and both types of skills should be encouraged in the classroom. One form of writing assignment follows:

Write ALL, SOME, and NONE sentences about this set of shapes. (See fig. 6.)

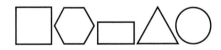

Fig. 6

Students in cooperative groups can then discuss, find counterexamples to, and assess the appropriateness of the sentences submitted.

Another useful type of writing assignment is the following:

Write a letter to a friend (or record a telephone conversation) explaining and describing what a rectangle is, how to find the area of a rectangle, and why the stated procedure works.

The next day, pairs of students should exchange their letters; the partners should discuss and edit each other's letter. Letters should be rewritten in light of the editing; the students should then try out their letter with a friend who is not familiar with the concept of the area of a rectangle.

In a cooperative learning setting, the teacher fosters communication and helps students construct connections among concepts, procedures, and approaches. Consider the following questions or exercises to be posed by the teacher:

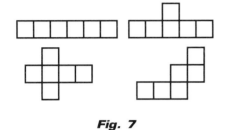

Fig. 7

- Is this true? Why? Can you find a counterexample? Is there a pattern? I wonder what would happen if....

- On your geoboard, show examples of a rectangle with four congruent sides; a parallelogram with four right angles; and a trapezoid with two equal angles.

- Describe some real-world examples of congruent figures and similar figures.

- Which shapes containing six adjoining squares can be folded to form a cube? (See fig. 7.) What other patterns of six adjoining squares can be folded to form a cube?

These open-ended questions or problems, which can have several correct answers, furnish opportunities for students to discuss their interpretations, write about their ideas, and expand their understanding. They also provide contexts through which teachers can assess students' abilities to connect geometric concepts, to communicate about mathematical ideas, and to think abstractly.

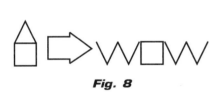

Fig. 8

Today's technology is useful in assisting students in developing and answering questions, in testing hypotheses, and in validating their own thinking. Students should be encouraged to explore and investigate patterns and problems in geometry by having calculators readily accessible. The use of Logo (Terrapin 1982) and the Geometric PreSupposer and the Geometric Supposer (Sunburst Communications 1986) computer software is especially suited for student investigations of geometric configurations and their properties and aids in developing spatial skills. With a brief introduction to Logo, students can be challenged to create designs such as those in figure 8. Using the Geometric Supposer, students can explore the question, Are the medians of a triangle concurrent? Finding that the medians are concurrent, the students should learn that this point of concurrency is the centroid, or center of gravity, of the triangle and should then enjoy putting their discovery to use in a physical context by cutting a triangle out of stiff cardboard, finding its centroid, and balancing and spinning the triangle on the tip of a pin.

From the previous sample of illustrative examples for implementing the *Curriculum and Evaluation Standards,* it is clear that students will need to engage in a wide variety of activities designed to develop higher-order thinking skills. Recent research on the van Hiele model of levels of thinking in geometry presents ideas and approaches particularly suited for middle grade students.

The van Hiele Model of Thinking in Geometry

Two Dutch middle school teachers, Dina van Hiele-Geldof (1984 [1957]) and Pierre van Hiele (1984 [1959]), were concerned about the difficulties their students encountered with geometry. They believed that the geometry they were teaching in grades 7–9 involved thinking at a relatively high "level" and that their students had not had sufficient experience in thinking at prerequisite lower "levels." Their research focused on levels of thinking in geometry and the role of instruction in helping students move from one level to the next. The van Hiele model of thinking, designed to help students gain insight into geometry, uses five levels to describe student behaviors: Level 0—Visual (e.g., judges shapes by their appearance); Level 1—Analysis (e.g., sees figures in terms of their components and discovers properties of a class of shapes); Level 2—Informal Deduction (e.g., logically interrelates previously discovered properties); Level 3—Deduction (e.g., proves theorems deductively); and Level 4—Rigor (e.g., establishes theorems in different postulational systems). The levels have specific characteristics: the levels are sequential; each level has its own language and set of symbols; what is implicit at one level is explicit at the next level (e.g., students use the properties of a class of shapes when classifying at Level 0, but they only begin to isolate and describe them when thinking at Level 1); and levels are subject to "reduction" by substituting a rote procedure for thinking. In comparing the "level" structure to Piaget's "stages," van Hiele considers the Piagetian approach to be a process of maturation, whereas the "level" approach is experienced-based and as such is a process of "apprenticeship" for the student.

For middle grade students, attention must be focused on helping students attain levels 0, 1, and 2 of the van Hiele model. The NCTM curriculum and evaluation standards for grades K–4 include a standard on Geometry and Spatial Sense (see also Del Grande [forthcoming]). Implementing this standard will give elementary school students many experiences at levels 0 and 1 for exploring geometry ideas. If students are having trouble learning geometry concepts, we might hypothesize, according to this model, that they are being taught at a higher level than they have attained. Moreover, two individuals (perhaps teacher and student or student and textbook author) who reason at different levels cannot understand each other because differing linguistic symbols and relationships are used; thus communication is difficult.

To give some insight into how Dina van Hiele-Geldof (1984 [1957]) introduced geometric concepts to her twelve-year-old middle school students, a brief description of her first lessons is presented here.

> The first lesson started by showing a cube made out of colored cardboard and a variety of cubes of different sizes (including dice, a cubic centimeter, and a skeletal model made with an Erector Set). The students counted the number of corners, sticks, and surfaces—thus the meanings for vertices, edges, and faces were introduced. They noticed that cubes could be formed from six squares. Right angles were also noticed; draftsman triangles were used to draw right angles. The term *perpendicular* was given concrete meaning by folding a piece of paper that had no straight edges. This folding produced a straight line segment; a second straight line segment was obtained by folding the paper such that the second folding line was perpendicular to the first folding line (see fig. 9). The angle between the folding lines was called a right angle. The students then constructed a cube with an Erector Set. With the help of strings, the diagonals of the cubes were formed; they discovered two different kinds of diagonals, which they called surface diagonals and interior diagonals. (Adapted from van Hiele-Geldof [1984 (1957)], pp. 20–21)

It is of interest to note that Dina van Hiele-Geldof's first lessons in geometry for her middle school students started with concrete three-dimensional shapes. During these experiences, the language and concepts of point, line, and plane naturally emerged by using physical models. Students are accustomed to handling and working with three-dimensional objects. This familiarity can serve as an important starting point for developing basic geometric concepts of point (vertex), line segment

"Reduction" of level: Having completed an investigation, a student discovers and justifies that the area of a parallelogram is the product of its base and altitude, thus showing level 2 thinking. If in all subsequent activities, the student is asked only to use the formula and find the area, given the numerical values for the base and altitude, the level of thinking has been "reduced" to one of simple computation (a rote procedure).

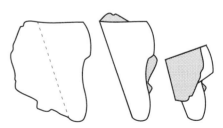

Fig. 9

(edge), parallel and perpendicular lines and planes, skew lines, angles in two and three dimensions, and polygons as faces of various polyhedra.

In a study applying the van Hiele model (Fuys, Geddes, and Tischler 1988), some sixth-grade students were asked, "What are the minimum properties needed to define a square?" They were given a set of "clue" cards from which they were to select the smallest number of clues needed to describe a square. The strategy of some students was to choose the fewest properties—they selected properties to eliminate the shapes they didn't want (Level 1 thinking). For example:

Juan: "Four sides" gives any quad.... "Opposite sides parallel" takes away all others except squares, rectangles, and parallelograms... "All right angles" leaves out parallelograms and I need one more..."all sides equal."

Other students responded deductively (Level 2 thinking):

Muriel: Obviously, if it has "four sides," it has "four angles" ...and it says "all right angles...." Once you know that, you don't need to know the "opposite angles are congruent...." Because it says "all sides are equal," you don't need "opposite sides are equal."

Andy: "Four sides" means "four angles...." "All sides equal" means "opposite sides are equal," so we don't need that.... Right angles are equal, so we don't need "opposite angles are equal."

Although most students arrived at a minimum set of properties for a square, the quality of thinking used differed. Andy and Muriel spontaneously proceeded to eliminate properties deductively (Level 2), and Juan proceeded by adding properties until a square was characterized (Level 1).

These same sixth graders did explorations on angle relationships on a grid, and all discovered the angle sum of a triangle (see Activity 8). The van Hieles often had their students reflect on the interrelationships among concepts and ideas they had learned by asking them to build a "family tree." An illustration of the "family tree" approach is given in Activities 11 and 13.

To move students from one thought level to the next within a topic, the van Hieles proposed a sequence of five "phases" of learning. These phases provide a prescription for organizing classroom instruction in geometry and are described as follows: (1) Inquiry—students discuss and develop questions on a topic to be explored; (2) Directed orientation—students explore sets of carefully sequenced activities; (3) Explicitation—students express explicit views and questions about inherent structures of their investigations; (4) Free orientation—students now encounter multistep tasks and gain experiences in finding their own way of resolving the tasks; and (5) Integration—students form an overview in which objects and relationships are unified and internalized into a new domain of thought. It should be noted the phases are not usually accomplished in a linear fashion; rather, students frequently cycle through several of the phases more than once before attaining a new domain of thought and thus reaching the next level.

The van Hiele approach to learning and teaching geometry clearly focuses on developing students' insight and higher levels of thinking. Thus, students need to have sustained periods of apprenticeship in which they engage in the types of investigations and activities presented in this book.

◆   ◆   ◆   ◆   ◆   ◆   ◆   ◆

Summary

The middle school geometry curriculum affords many opportunities for students to explore their environment and to learn and enjoy many new, exciting, and fascinating aspects and applications of mathematics in their world. A case has been made for establishing a classroom atmosphere that encourages students to explore and investigate geometry problems, to ask questions, to engage in divergent thinking, and to use logical reasoning to develop cogent and convincing arguments. A sampling of such explorations and investigations has been highlighted in the discussion above. A more comprehensive set of such activities and supplementary visual materials to assist in the development of these activities is presented in the next section, entitled **Sample Activities**.

The flowchart (fig. 10) indicates the organization and sequence of the sample activities. Most activities involve student investigations leading to discoveries, pattern finding, making and testing conjectures, and problem solving.

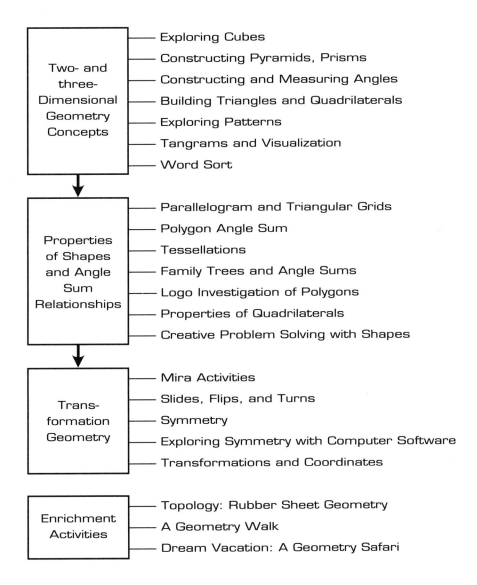

Two- and three-Dimensional Geometry Concepts
— Exploring Cubes
— Constructing Pyramids, Prisms
— Constructing and Measuring Angles
— Building Triangles and Quadrilaterals
— Exploring Patterns
— Tangrams and Visualization
— Word Sort

Properties of Shapes and Angle Sum Relationships
— Parallelogram and Triangular Grids
— Polygon Angle Sum
— Tessellations
— Family Trees and Angle Sums
— Logo Investigation of Polygons
— Properties of Quadrilaterals
— Creative Problem Solving with Shapes

Trans-formation Geometry
— Mira Activities
— Slides, Flips, and Turns
— Symmetry
— Exploring Symmetry with Computer Software
— Transformations and Coordinates

Enrichment Activities
— Topology: Rubber Sheet Geometry
— A Geometry Walk
— Dream Vacation: A Geometry Safari

Fig. 10

SAMPLE ACTIVITIES

In this section are a variety of activities appropriate for the middle grades. Each cluster of activities contains Teaching Notes and references to other sources for additional activities. The activities are designed around geometry topics in the mathematics curricula for grades 5 through 8 and incorporate many of the features recommended in the NCTM *Curriculum and Evaluation Standards for School Mathematics*—namely, student investigations, activity-oriented explorations (constructions and the use of manipulatives), student writing, cooperative learning, spatial visualization activities, use of technology, mathematical connections, van Hiele type of approaches to developing thinking and reasoning skills, problem solving with "what if" extensions, and real-world applications.

Curriculum Topics

Below are listed the curriculum topics around which the activities cluster:

A. Two- and Three-Dimensional Geometry Concepts: Activities 1–7

B. Relationships among Properties of Shapes Including Angle Sums: Activities 8–14

C. Transformation Geometry: Activities 15–19

D. Enrichment Topics: Activities 20–22

The first three clusters are sequential and interdependent in that students will need some of the background concepts and vocabulary developed in cluster A for activities in clusters B and C. Many of the activities within each cluster are self-contained. Motivational hands-on activities, problems, real-world applications, or puzzle situations are provided to entice student explorations. The fourth cluster presents some additional enrichment activities.

Vocabulary

Mathematical vocabulary is an important part of mathematical learning. Middle school students probably have seen a lot of geometry vocabulary; meaningful contexts for review and for clarification are essential. The hands-on activities, cooperative learning, and "journal writes" included in each cluster provide contexts for students to "talk" geometry. Students should not repeat rotely learned vocabulary with little understanding of what they are saying. They need to reflect on what they have learned, integrate the concepts with previous experiences, and initially use everyday vocabulary and familiar concrete experiences to describe the concepts. This will assist with the acquisition of vocabulary and give greater meaning to new vocabulary.

A description in plain language is a criterion of the degree of understanding that has been reached.

Albert Einstein

Objectives and Materials

For each cluster of activities, objectives are stated that are direct consequences of the NCTM *Curriculum and Evaluation Standards* for grades 5 through 8 on mathematics as problem solving, mathematics as communication, mathematics as reasoning, mathematical connections, and geometry and spatial sense. Some activities address multiple objectives. Many of the activities involve hands-on experiences using inexpensive teacher-made or student-made materials. The hands-on activities provide valuable experiences in spatial visualization for students. The materials needed for each activity are listed. Each cluster of activities has blackline masters in the Appendix, which are numbered to correspond to the appropriate activity.

Activity Sheets

An *activity sheet* is furnished for each activity. There are two formats for activity sheets. Many are designed to be given to students to work on in small cooperative groups or independently. Others might be done more appropriately by the teacher and the class working together; if used in this way, the activity sheet might be considered a script for the teacher. This is especially true if the class has limited reading skills. Some activity sheets may require several lessons to complete, or the teacher might choose to complete only portions of an activity sheet with a class.

Teaching Notes

Each group of activities contains a brief set of *teaching notes* to provide some guidance to the teacher on the design and intended use of the activities. Teaching ideas are presented within the notes as a guide to developing the activities. Answers to key questions on the activity sheets used by the students in their explorations and investigations are provided in the teaching notes. Copies of the activity sheets can be duplicated for the students.

Computer Technology

The activities involving *computer technology* make use of the Geometric PreSupposer and the microworld of Logo. Other software focusing on informal geometry is commercially available but has not been included in these activities except as references.

Evaluation Notes

Evaluation notes to the teacher are included at the end of the teaching notes for each cluster of activities. As stated in the Preface, new approaches to evaluation need to be used.

Evaluation is an ongoing task. Teachers can learn a lot about students' progress in geometry by being observant during class activities. A sample checklist of things to be aware of and to find evidence for includes—

- improvement in students' thinking skills and van Hiele level of thinking;
- improvement in students' visualization skills;
- improvement in students' explanations and ability to justify conclusions;
- increase in students' self-confidence;
- increase in students' willingness to explore ideas, make and test conjectures, take risks, and engage in divergent thinking;
- increase in students' repertoire of problem-solving strategies;
- increase in students' dynamic interaction with their environment;
- greater student awareness of real-world applications of geometry and logical thinking;
- greater willingness to propose and consider alternative solutions to problems;
- greater ability of students to recognize connections between geometry and other aspects of mathematics.

In this book, the use of student *portfolios* is recommended for evaluating students' written work. Students assemble in their portfolios the best products of their work: their journal writing; their growing glossary; their models; their investigations, discoveries, conjectures, and verifications; their analyses of specific problems and possible extensions; their creative activities; their computer explorations; and their projects. In the evaluation notes, some illustrative examples are given.

◆ ◆ ◆ ◆ ◆ ◆ ◆ ◆ ◆

CLUSTER A
TWO- AND THREE-DIMENSIONAL
GEOMETRY CONCEPTS

Activity 1: Exploring Cubes

Activity 2: Constructing Pyramids, Prisms, and Other Solids
  a. Constructing Pyramids and Prisms
  b. Cylinders, Cones, Spheres, and Circles
  c. Extension: More about Solids

Activity 3: Constructing and Measuring Angles
  a. Constructing Angles
  b. Angle Measurement

Activity 4: Building Triangles and Quadrilaterals
  a. Building Triangles and Quadrilaterals
  b. Geometric PreSupposer Investigation of Triangles

Activity 5: Exploring Patterns
  a. Figurate (Polygonal) Numbers
  b. Discovering Patterns with Lines
  c. Discovering Patterns with Tiles and Sticks
  d. Patterns on a Geoboard
  e. Pythagorean Theorem

Activity 6: Tangrams and Visualization

Activity 7: Word Sort

OBJECTIVES OF CLUSTER A:

1. To provide hands-on experiences in constructing two- and three-dimensional shapes

2. To develop the ability to visualize two- and three-dimensional shapes and to recognize them in the environment

3. To observe and identify properties related to two- and three-dimensional shapes

4. To develop and review geometry vocabulary and concepts and provide opportunities for students to converse about geometric ideas

5. To create models of networks of solids

6. To compare and contrast properties of shapes through the use of examples and nonexamples (i.e., the "concept card" approach)

7. To develop and assess thinking skills such as sorting, classifying, and making and testing conjectures

8. To experience the use of inductive reasoning by gathering data in varied geometric settings, finding patterns in the data, and making generalizations

9. To investigate properties of geometric shapes by using computer technology

10. To engage in explorations designed to enhance spatial visualization skills

◆　　　◆　　　◆　　　◆　　　◆　　　◆　　　◆　　　◆

TEACHING NOTES FOR CLUSTER A:

A number of the introductory activities engage the students in the actual construction of two- and three-dimensional models. See Activities 1, 2, 3, and 4. The construction of cubes, pyramids, prisms, other polyhedra, and two-dimensional shapes provides a context for developing basic concepts, basic vocabulary, and spatial visualization skills.

A "concept card" approach is useful in building mathematical ideas. See Activities 2 and 3. On a concept card, both examples and nonexamples are shown. On the basis of this information, students are to decide which of some further illustrations are examples of the concept and to provide other examples and nonexamples. Finally, they are to verbalize a description or a rule for the concept. Working on a concept card activity allows students to develop and use the higher-order thinking skills of comparing, contrasting, and discriminating, of formulating and testing conjectures, and then of summarizing their ideas verbally in a good description or definition of the concept. It's a great way to have students create definitions of mathematical concepts—not just geometry concepts! Here is an example (fig. 11).

A number of activities are designed to engage students in an active search for patterns (see Activity 5). Searching for patterns is an important strategy in problem exploration. Through varied experiences in inductive reasoning, students develop new approaches to problem solving.

Listed below are specific teaching notes for each activity with an indication of materials needed, teaching ideas, and answers to key questions.

Activity 1: Exploring Cubes

Materials: Assorted boxes and models of rectangular prisms (including cubes); toothpicks and minimarshmallows (for best results, allow marshmallows to dry out a day or two before use); square grid or dot paper; isometric dot paper (optional); tagboard to make networks of cubes; cellophane tape; copies of Activity Sheet 1 for students

The activity sheet provides the script to be followed in the lesson. Cooperative groups work well in this activity. Questions should be asked to assist students to think of basic geometric concepts and to develop vocabulary. Concepts such as point, vertex, line, edge, parallel and perpendicular lines, skew lines, plane, angle, right angle, parallel and perpendicular planes, square, rectangle, diagonal, and so on, naturally arise in student discussions and in response to questions. These activities give students an opportunity to see, touch, and manipulate tangible embodiments of the concepts. They allow students to build visualization skills as they study relationships among attributes of geometric objects and figures. Students might draw some of the networks on tagboard and construct cubes and open boxes. Students might make up their own versions of creating a "building" with given front, side, and top views to challenge their classmates.

Answers: There are twelve different pentominoes. Pentominoes are not considered "different" if the same figure can be obtained by slide, flip, or turn motions. Eight of the twelve pentominoes can be folded into open boxes (i.e., a cube without a lid).

Extensions:

a. *Spatial Visualization* (Winter, Lappan, Phillips, and Fitzgerald 1986) "Spatial Visualization" (Lappan and Winter 1982)
b. *Boxes, Squares and Other Things* (Walter 1970)
c. "Pentominoes Revisited" (Onslow 1990)

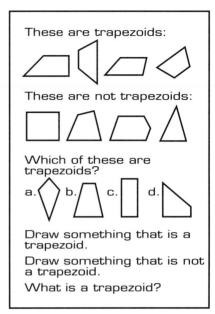

These are trapezoids:

These are not trapezoids:

Which of these are trapezoids?

a. b. c. d.

Draw something that is a trapezoid.

Draw something that is not a trapezoid.

What is a trapezoid?

Fig. 11

Square pyramid

Lateral edges meet at a point.
Lateral faces are triangles.

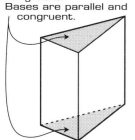

Base

Triangular prism

Lateral edges are parallel and congruent.
Bases are parallel and congruent.

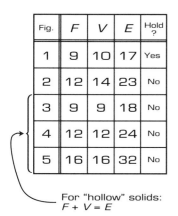

Fig. 12

Fig.	F	V	E	Hold?
1	9	10	17	Yes
2	12	14	23	No
3	9	9	18	No
4	12	12	24	No
5	16	16	32	No

For "hollow" solids:
$F + V = E$

Fig. 13

Activity 2a: Constructing Pyramids and Prisms

Materials: Models of pyramids and prisms; straws and pipe cleaners, or D-Stix and connectors, for each cooperative group; copies of Activity Sheet 2a for students

In this investigation, each group uses straws and pieces of pipe cleaners (or D-Stix and connectors) to construct pyramids and prisms with different polygonal bases by following the instructions given on the activity sheets. The concept card approach (described earlier) is used in these activities. Data gathered from these investigations are used by the students to make and verify conjectures. The teacher's role in this activity is one of facilitator—assisting, clarifying, raising questions, and encouraging conjectures. Groups should share their findings. Many different patterns will be discovered. Have they discovered a pattern that holds for both pyramids and prisms? In particular, have they discovered Euler's theorem: $V + F = E + 2$, where V = number of vertices, F = number of faces, and E = number of edges? Basic properties of prisms and pyramids (bases, lateral edges, lateral faces) should be discussed (fig. 12). For related activites, see Hilton and Pedersen (1988).

Activity 2b: Cylinders, Cones, Spheres, and Circles

Materials: Collection of real-world models of cylinders, cones, and spheres; clay; compasses; lids from circular containers; rectangular sheets of paper; cut-out circles; scissors; cellophane tape; copies of Activity Sheet 2c for students; globe of the world and Mercator map of the world (optional)

The activity sheet serves as the script to be followed in the lesson. These activities are designed to enhance students' spatial visualization skills and to enlarge their ability to recognize and find applications of geometry in their environment. Students should be encouraged to create their own models and designs (which may result in attractive bulletin board displays) and to create an organized collection of illustrations related to geometry ideas from newspapers, magazines, and photographs. For additional design projects, see Pohl (1986).

Activity 2c: Extension: More about Solids

Materials: Copies of Activity Sheet 2c for students who want a challenge

In this activity, students explore more complex polyhedra to determine if Euler's theorem holds or if it needs to be modified for shapes having particular characteristics. Students' data should include the results shown in figure 13.

Activity 3a: Constructing Angles

Materials: Copies of models of rays for constructing angles (see Appendix); paper fasteners; scissors; scraps of newspaper; copies of Activity Sheet 3a for students

The activities are designed to develop an intuitive concept of angle by having students construct, rotate, and use the angle models in a variety of settings. Descriptions of the "clock" angle should lead to developing the meanings of right, acute, obtuse, and straight angles. Congruent angles should be illustrated and discussed by students, who should note that the physical length of the model rays is not relevant.

From folding the scrap of paper, the students have created their own personal "right-angle tester"; they should preserve it and use it to determine whether angles are greater than, less than, or equal to a right angle. The L-square on the blackline master in the Appendix is another form of right-angle tester. A comparison of two right angles and a straight angle should be made. Students should explore rotating the two rays of an angle to form a straight angle and discover (describe) that a straight angle is formed by two rays with a common vertex that extend in opposite directions to form a straight line. (The difference between a straight angle and a straight line segment should be noted; in particular, a straight angle has a vertex and is measured in angle units (degrees); a straight line segment has endpoints and is measured in linear units.)

Extension: Students may point out in the classroom angles formed by two or three walls (planes) or angles formed by the pages of an opened book; this provides an opportunity to discuss dihedral angles (formed by the intersection of two half planes); trihedral angles (formed by three half planes intersecting at a point, such as at the corner of the room where two walls and the ceiling intersect); and polyhedral angles (such as the angle formed at the vertex of a square prism or a pentagonal pyramid).

The ideas presented in this lesson lay the groundwork for later activities that develop the concepts of angle measurement and other angle pairs: complementary, supplementary, and vertical. In future lessons on angle pairs, the angle models developed in this activity could be used extensively. For example, the optional problem lays the foundation for developing the concepts of alternate interior and corresponding angles of parallel lines.

Activity 3b: Angle Measurement

Materials: Tracing paper; copies of Activity Sheet 3b for students

Use this activity to develop the concept of angle measurement. As in all initial measurement lessons, students should begin with nonstandard units to estimate and measure and then discover the need for a standard unit. In this example, the wedges of different sizes (A, B, and C are nonstandard units) should be used to estimate and then measure the sizes of angles *P, Q, R,* and *S*. This activity is then extended to estimate and measure in terms of D wedges (where each D wedge represents one degree—the standard unit).

Students will find tracing paper useful in this activity. The use of a nonstandard unit to measure the angles in a triangle and in a quadrilateral lays the groundwork for later lessons on angle sums for polygons.

Activity 4a: Building Triangles and Quadrilaterals

Materials: Geostrips (see Appendix) and paper fasteners or D-Stix and connectors or different-length straws and pipe cleaners; copies of Activity Sheet 4a for students

This activity gives the students hands-on, concrete experiences in constructing and examining properties of various types of triangles and quadrilaterals. Working in cooperative groups, students should complete the investigations outlined in Activity Sheet 4a. As the teacher circulates among the groups, questions should be raised, alternative issues and strategies might be posed for consideration, and explanations and justifications of students' conjectures should be sought. Groups should share and compare the observations and the conjectures made in their investigations. Students should recognize that three noncollinear points determine a plane and that the triangle is a rigid figure. A quadrilateral is flexible; the fourth point may not lie in the same plane as the other three points. When the two intersecting diagonals of a quadrilateral are drawn in, triangles are formed and the quadrilateral becomes rigid.

Students should be encouraged to discover the use of polygons and polyhedra in real-world settings. For a fine collection of slides, see *Geometry in Our World* (Engelhardt 1987). Also, you may want to focus students' attention on the property of rigidity by exploring such questions as these: Have you noticed triangles in the construction of a bridge? Why do you think engineers and architects use triangular shapes in their construction work?

Activity 4b: Geometric PreSupposer Investigation of Triangles

Materials: Geometric PreSupposer software; computers; copies of Activity Sheet 4b for students. For other geometric investigation software, see Elastic Lines.

Communication between students is best promoted if two students work at each computer, taking turns. Little introduction to the program is necessary. However, an overview in a whole-class setting of the menus the students will encounter and a brief demonstration of the potential of the commands selected are good ways to set the stage. Students should not use the Geometric PreSupposer without some concrete hands-on experiences with models of angles and triangles, as described in Activities 3 and 4a.

Extension: The activity can be extended by having the class create a data base. The pairs of students type in their data and then enter the data into a data base such as AppleWorks or MECC Create-A-Base. After all the data have been entered, the students can display (and print out) the information in line form as follows (E—equilateral; I—isosceles; S—scalene):

Type E, I, or S	Side A	Side B	Side C	Angle A	Angle B	Angle C

At first, the data will be mixed up because each team will be entering data for triangles of all three types. However, by displaying data for TYPE E, the students will readily see patterns about the angles and the sides. Similar inspections can be made of the other two types of triangles. Alternatively, the students can simply alphabetize the records by the field TYPE, which will then display all the E triangles first, then all the I triangles, then all the S triangles. Either way, the usefulness of the data base (as a technological tool) in organizing and then displaying the data in a desired form will help the students in this exploratory activity. For an extended discussion for using conjecturing and microcomputers to teach geometry, see Chazen and Houde (1989).

Activities 5a-5e: Exploring Patterns

Materials: Copies of Activity Sheets 5a–5e for students; for Activity 5c, square tiles and small sticks (parts of toothpicks); for Activity 5d, geoboards and rubber bands, dot paper; for Activity 5e, rulers, sheets of graph paper, strips of the same grid graph paper, tangram pieces, geoboards and rubber bands, the videotape: *The Theorem of Pythagoras* (Apostol 1988).

Patterns of Odds and Evens:

One directive of the *Curriculum and Evaluation Standards* (NCTM 1989) is to interrelate topics in mathematics. A lesson for the middle grades on the "geometry of odds and evens," described here, illustrates how students can use the language of geometry to deal with some problems in number theory involving odds and evens. Moreover, the lesson illustrates how students' van Hiele levels of thinking about odds and evens can be fostered—the students at the beginning level think of odds and evens as a list of numbers, then form a geometric definition for them, and finally, discover and informally prove some properties about the sums of odds and evens.

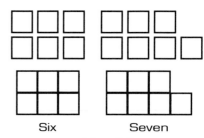

Six   Seven

Fig. 14

When asked to tell what an even or an odd number is, students often give a list: the even numbers are 2, 4, 6, 8, 10, 12, . . . ; the odd numbers are 1, 3, 5, 7, 9, 11, ... An even number is "a number like one of those in the list; you get them by skip counting by 2s." Students can be asked to represent odd and even numbers by using sets of objects (e.g., cubes) or diagrams (fig. 14) for the numbers 6 and 7.

When asked "Why do you think that 6 is called an even number and 7 is called an odd number," students can begin to formulate an informal definition for "even" and "odd." For example, "an even number is one that has everything matched up"; "an odd number is one where there is one 'odd' square at the end." The students then understand why those numbers are called "odd" and "even." They think of an even number as a rectangle with two even rows, whereas an odd number is a shape like a rectangle with one extra square on the top or bottom row.

Students can go on to discover some properties of even and odd numbers under addition. Experimentation leads them to discover that the sum of two evens is even, the sum of two odds is even, and the sum of an odd and an even is odd. When asked to explain, many will respond, "Well, I tried lots of examples, and it always came out that way." This inductive thinking is fine and shows how students can discover properties by experimentation (van Hiele Level 1). Some students may use another approach, explaining that "an even plus an even is an even because it's like putting two long, even rectangles together, which makes a longer even rectangle." Also, "When two odd shapes are put together, they make a long even shape, hence the sum of two odd numbers must be an even number" (fig. 15).

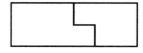

Fig. 15

Thus, students are informally "proving" these rules by using geometric representations for odd and even numbers. In terms of the van Hiele model, they are now indicating Level 2 thinking, namely, informal deductive explanations that logically link properties of objects (in this case, odd and even numbers).

What's next? The students might discover and explain other rules for adding odd and even numbers. For example, what is the sum of three odd numbers? This problem can be approached on Level 1 by experimentation. On Level 2, the students might use three odd-number shapes, which when put together yield an odd-number shape, or use the rules they just explained, namely, "two odds make an even, which when added to another odd makes an odd." The "family tree" (fig. 16) captures the logical parts of this explanation.

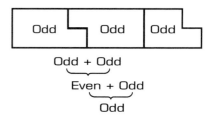

Odd + Odd

Even + Odd

Odd

Fig. 16

Students can be challenged to formulate and prove other properties: What must the sum of two consecutive numbers be: odd or even? What must be the sum of any four consecutive numbers or any even number of consecutive numbers? What can we say about the sum of an odd number of consecutive numbers? In terms of the van Hiele levels, the students are building an informal network of logical relationships.

This initiation into informal deduction with odds and evens is made possible by the friendly geometric representation of these numbers. We could use algebraic representation to derive such rules (e.g., $2n$ for even, $2n + 1$ for odd), but that work may be too formal for some middle grade students. Thus, using geometry to represent odd and even numbers empowers students to discover and explore deductively a mathematical topic. This experience can lead to explorations about other geometric shapes of numbers (e.g., square, oblong, triangular).

Activities 5a–5e give students experience in the use of inductive reasoning by having them gather data in a variety of geometric settings, find patterns in the data, and make generalizations. In Activity 5a, real-world settings of figurate (polygonal) and pyramidal numbers should be considered (e.g., setting up bowling pins, stacking cans in store displays). In Activities 5b and 5c, encourage students to look for similarities and differences in the patterns discovered. Sets of congruent tiles should be available for student use; many students need this hands-on visual approach, rather than a mere diagram, to assist them in gathering the data. Upper middle grade students might be encouraged to express in algebraic form the patterns they discover. In Activity 5d, students use spatial visualization skills to represent shapes concretely (on the geoboard) and semiabstractly (on dot paper); they also use ideas of motion geometry (e.g., rotation and reflection of shapes). In Activity 5e, from the visual representations of the triangles, students should conjecture that $a^2 + b^2$ is greater than c^2 for an acute triangle and less than c^2 for an obtuse triangle. Part 4 gives real-world applications of the Pythagorean theorem in two and three dimensions.

Extension for Activity 5e: Show and discuss the videotape *The Theorem of Pythagoras* (Apostol 1988). This excellent video shows real-world uses of the Pythagorean theorem and gives some historical background. In the "challenge" problem, the students create the square root spiral (fig. 17).

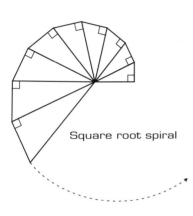

Square root spiral

Fig. 17

Activity 6: Tangrams and Visualization

Materials: Tangrams (see Appendix); scissors; copies of Activity Sheet 6 for students

This puzzle is rich in possiblities not only in geometry and spatial skills but also in problem solving in arithmetic. Note how item 9 can be extended to work with fractions, decimals, and percents, thus making connections between geometry and arithmetic. The activity also furnishes some experience in motion geometry as students transform a square into various other shapes. It is possible to have the students construct their own tangram puzzles through a paper-folding activity. This approach is described in many books and articles on tangrams (see Hill [1987], pp. 133–37).

Extension: "Visualization" (see Maletsky [1987], pp. 7–12) focuses on two- and three-dimensional visualization of polygons and polyhedra. It can be used as an enrichment or special project activity. The questions raised on the last page of "Visualization" are particularly interesting and challenging. Also see "Tangrams" by Bazik (1988), pp. 42–47.

Activity 7: Word Sort

Materials: Envelopes containing cut-up copies of all (or selected) words on the Word Sort sheet (one envelope for each cooperative group)

Several students might be asked to prepare the envelopes with the cut-out shapes ahead of time. The activity is designed to develop higher-order thinking skills. Ideas of sorting, comparing, contrasting, and "guessing my rule" are included. As in all cooperative learning activities, the teacher's role is to observe thinking strategies, listen to each group's explanations, and propose "what if" questions (What if I moved several of your words this way [moving some words]. What might my rule be?).

Students may find many ways to sort the words. They may, for example, decide that all words relating to angles, or to angle pairs, belong together, and in the process will probably, as a group, review what each angle-related word means. They may decide that some words relate to two-dimensional geometry, whereas others relate to three dimensions. Some words relate to classes of things (acute), whereas others describe relations between things (intersecting, congruent).

Students will be reviewing a great deal of geometry vocabulary and possibly will be filling in gaps in their own knowledge through conversation with their classmates. But they will also be exercising higher-order thinking skills by looking for similarities and differences, making analogies, and trying to guess other students' rules.

EVALUATION NOTES FOR ACTIVITIES 1–7

Reasons for evaluation:

- To assess students' grasp of concepts; to discover any student misconceptions
- To observe and encourage precision, accuracy, and neatness in students' work
- To judge students' knowledge so subsequent lessons can be planned
- To evaluate students' logical thinking and their recognition of mathematical concepts in the real world
- To assess students' ability to discover patterns and use inductive reasoning to make conjectures; to reflect on their own thinking; and to extend mathematics learning beyond the mathematics classroom
- To assess students' higher-order thinking about and comprehension of basic shapes and their interrelationships.

Activities 1 and 2

Teacher assignments for student portfolios:

1. Complete a "journal write": Write about a cube, telling all you know or have observed about it; describe some of the properties you have investigated or discovered; include a sketch, network, and your answers to exercise 3 of Activity 1.
2. Select some of the models of three-dimensional geometric figures you have constructed and include them in your portfolio; describe the models.
3. From magazines and newspapers, find and organize a set of photographs showing the use of two- and three-dimensional geometric figures in the real world. Briefly describe your collection.
4. Create a growing "glossary" of geometry words.

Evaluation of portfolios:

1. "Journal writes" can be evaluated on the basis of the appropriateness of the vocabulary, the completeness of the properties noted, the networks, and the sketch.
2. Models can be evaluated on the basis of precision, accuracy, and neatness.

Activities 3 and 4

Teacher assignments for student portfolios:

1. Write a letter to a friend who knows nothing about triangles (or quadrilaterals) and describe what you have discovered about triangles (or quadrilaterals); compare and contrast different shapes and note particular properties; explain how triangles (or quadrilaterals) are used in the real world.
2. Include models of angles, triangles, and quadrilaterals in your portfolio.
3. Create a "concept card" for a geometry topic you have studied (e.g., vertical angles, supplementary angles, isosceles triangle, rhombus).

Include the answers to the various parts of your concept card on the back of the card.

4. Prepare a laboratory report of an investigation you completed using the Geometric PreSupposer. Indicate the problem being investigated, the shapes examined, the observations made, the data collected, and the conjectures made. Also include verifications, any unanswered questions, and possible extensions of the investigation.

Evaluation of portfolios:

1. The "letter to a friend" can be evaluated on the basis of the appropriateness of the vocabulary, the completeness of the properties described, the clarity of the explanations, and the breadth of the real-world applications noted.

2. Models can be evaluated on the basis of precision, accuracy, and neatness.

3. The "concept card" can be assessed on the basis of the correctness, the appropriateness, and the variety of the examples and nonexamples presented, the precision and accuracy of the drawings made, the logical thinking involved, the overall presentation, and the answers supplied on the back of the card. Student-made concept cards can also be given to other students to respond to and to evaluate; students learn a great deal from peer evaluation of their work.

4. The laboratory report can be assessed on the basis of the thoroughness of the investigation in light of the problem posed, the logical thinking and the analysis of the results obtained, the overall comprehensiveness of the report, and the significance of the extensions being considered.

Activities 5 and 6

Teacher assignments for student portfolios:

1. Complete Activity Sheets 5a–5e.

2. Complete a "journal write": Write about your experiences in "pattern finding" and in making conjectures; describe some of the strategies you used in searching for a pattern; describe some of your successes and nonsuccesses in "pattern finding"; comment on your search for patterns outside the mathematics class, for example, in other subjects and in everyday living.

3. Create projects to display on a bulletin board or in a mathematics exhibit or at a mathematics fair. Include geometric designs, solids, tangram activities, and games. Each "creation" should be appropriately mounted for display and must be accompanied by a carefully written description of how the project was thought out and an explanation of the mathematics and the patterns involved.

Evaluation of portfolios and activities:

1. Students' ability to discover patterns and make correct conjectures can be assessed on the basis of their work on the activity sheets.

2. From the "journal write," a teacher can assess the student's awareness of strategies for "pattern finding"; the student's ability to reflect on his or her own thinking processes; and the student's ability to recognize and extend the "pattern finding" approach beyond the mathematics class.

3. Students' projects for display can be evaluated on the basis of creativity, innovation, originality, accuracy, and precision and on the students' ability to explain the evolution of the project, its patterns, and its mathematical basis.

Activity 7

1. This Word Sort can serve as a culminating assessment activity for a class (working in cooperative groups) at the conclusion of a unit on the basic concepts of geometry.

2. A group (or groups) of students may be asked to show their arrangement(s) to the rest of the class and to challenge the class to guess the rule(s) behind their arrangement(s).

Evaluation of the activity:

Students' knowledge, vocabulary, and higher-order thinking skills can be evaluated as the teacher circulates among the groups, making observations, raising questions, and asking for explanations or justifications of the various word sorts done by the groups. Students may explain that they looked for similarities and differences, noticed relationships, or recognized classes of things.

ACTIVITY 1
EXPLORING CUBES

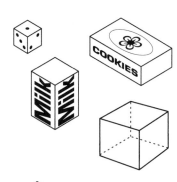

1. Where have you seen objects like these before?

   What do you call them?

   What are some objects like these that you have seen in your home, school, and community?

   Here are a square prism and a rectangular prism.

   Are these cubes? Why or why not?

2. Create your own skeletal models of a cube using toothpicks and minimarshmallows.

   Compare your model with others in your group. Ask these questions:

   How many toothpicks did you use?

   How many marshmallows did you use?

   Are there any parallel lines? Perpendicular lines? Skew lines? Explain.

   Are there any parallel planes? Perpendicular planes? Explain.

   Discuss and record the different properties each member of the group observes.

3. 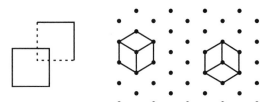 One way to sketch a cube is to draw two squares as shown on the left and then to connect the corresponding vertices of the squares. (An alternative approach is to sketch cubes by using isometric dot paper as shown.)

   Make a sketch of your cube in the space below and label the vertices with different capital letters. Using your diagram—

   name a pair of parallel lines;

   name a pair of perpendicular lines;

   name a pair of skew lines;

   name a square;

   determine how many squares are needed to form a cube;

   name a right angle;

   name a face diagonal;

   name a diagonal of the cube.

Is it possible to name a rectangle in your diagram that is not a square? Explain.

4. Here are some pictures of number cubes.

Which of the pictures above could be a view of a number cube that is made by folding a pattern like this?

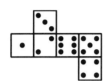

This flattened-out pattern of a cube is called a "network" of a cube.

How many squares are needed to form the network of a cube?

5. A flat pattern (or network) made up of five squares where each square must share an edge with another square is called a *pentomino*. Here are some examples of pentominoes:

On pieces of square grid or dot paper, each member of the group should sketch some pentominoes.

How many different pentominoes are there?

How many of these pentominoes can be folded to form an open box?

6. Models of buildings are frequently created using cubes, and then front, side, and top views of the model are drawn.

For example:

Can you make out of cubes a "building" that has these top, front, and side views? Sketch your result.

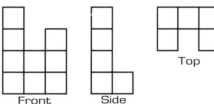

Front   Side   Top

Sometimes the "floor plan" can be recorded by showing the number of cubes needed in each part.

For example:

4	2	3
1	0	1

Does this "floor plan" match your "building"?

7. Challenge: How many cubes were needed to build the design in this figure? Explain several different ways of solving this problem.

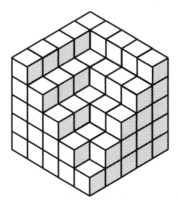

EXPLORING

Straws can be joined together at the ends with pieces of pipe cleaners.

Try it!

Build something that has no "loose ends."

Compare it with someone else's construction.

What questions could you ask about your construction?

? ? ? ? ? ? ? ? ? ?

Did you ask these questions?

> Does your construction lie flat on your desk, or does it stand up?
> What shapes can you see in your construction?
> How many straws did you use?
> Is your construction rigid or will it bend?
> Does your construction remind you of a real object?

What else can you make?

SOME CONSTRUCTIONS

Make a square with straws.

At each corner, attach a straw. (Use the same-length straw at each corner.)

Join these four straws at a point.

Does this remind you of anything? (Hint: Think of Egypt!)

You have made a *pyramid*—actually, it is a square pyramid.

These are also *pyramids*:

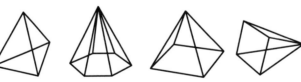

These are *not* pyramids:

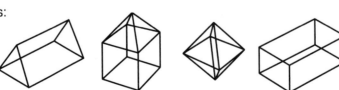

Make something that is a pyramid. Draw it.

Make something that is *not* a pyramid. Draw it.

How would you describe a pyramid to your friend over the telephone?

ACTIVITY 2A (CONTINUED)
CONSTRUCTING PYRAMIDS AND PRISMS

A PATTERN FOR PYRAMIDS

Look at your square pyramid.

It has 5 vertices. That is, there are 5 joining points.

It has 8 edges. That is, there are 8 straws.

It has 5 faces. That is, there is 1 square face on the bottom and 4 triangular faces around the sides.

Make a triangular pyramid. Count its vertices, its edges, and its faces. How many of each does the triangular pyramid have?

Fill in the missing numbers in this chart. Make the pyramids to help you count.

	Type of pyramid	Number of vertices	Number of faces	Number of edges
Triangle	Triangular pyramid			
Square	Square pyramid	5	5	5
Pentagon	Pentagonal pyramid			
Hexagon	Hexagonal pyramid			

Do you see any number patterns? Describe them.

More questions!

Suppose that you made a pyramid whose base looked like this:

Without making it, how could you tell how many vertices, edges, and faces it had?

Mayleen made a pyramid using 20 straws. Can you describe her pyramid?

Milo says that he made a pyramid using 13 straws (but it fell apart so he can't show it to you!). Do you believe him? Why or why not?

ACTIVITY 2A (CONTINUED)
CONSTRUCTING PYRAMIDS AND PRISMS

A PATTERN FOR PRISMS

In the previous activity you explored some properties of pyramids. Here is another type of solid.

These are *prisms*.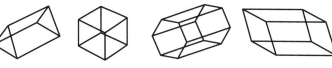

These are *not* prisms:

Make something that is a prism.

How would you describe a prism to your friend over the telephone?

Fill in the missing numbers in this chart.

Type of prism	Number of vertices	Number of faces	Number of edges
Triangular prism			
Square prism	8	6	12
Pentagonal prism			
Hexagonal prism			

Do you see any number patterns? Describe them.

More questions!

Suppose that you made a prism whose base looked like this:

Without making it, how could you tell how many vertices, edges, and faces it would have?

Yvonne made a prism with 24 straws. Can you describe her prism?

Could you ever make a solid that was both a prism and a pyramid? Why or why not?

Compare pyramids and prisms. How are they alike? How are they different?

ACTIVITY 2B
CYLINDERS, CONES, SPHERES, AND CIRCLES

CYLINDERS AND CONES

Have you ever seen a water tower or a rocket
that looks like this?

Have you seen other solids that are not polyhedra, that are not
bounded by plane surfaces, and that can be rolled? Describe some.

What real-world objects look like the pictures below? Name and describe them.

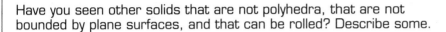

Figure A has two parallel bases that are congruent circles. Try rolling a rectangular sheet of paper so
two edges can be taped together evenly. Does your figure look like A?

Figure B has one base that is a circle. Try taking
part of a circular disk and taping the two straight
edges (*OA* and *OB*) together evenly as shown in
the figure at the right. Does your figure look like B?

SPHERES AND CIRCLES

Figure C has no flat surfaces; every point on the surface is the same distance from the center. In what
sports have you used an object of this shape? What fruits do you eat that have this shape? How is this
shape used in science class? In studying geography?

What geometric shape is the equator? What geometric
shape are the parallels of latitude? What geometric
shape is the Greenwich meridian?

You have found an old map that says a treasure is buried
10 meters from a marked rock in a nearby park. Where
would you look for the treasure?

What if you find an additional clue that says the treasure
is also 8 meters from a famous old tree in the park.
Would you change your plans for digging for the
treasure? Explain.

Why do we use round tires on our bikes and cars and
round wheels on our skates and skateboards instead of square ones?

NETWORKS OF THREE-DIMENSIONAL SHAPES

How can circles and rectangles be used to create three-dimensional models? Which of the networks
(flat patterns) below could be used to create a cylinder? Justify your conclusion.

What flat pattern would you make to create a cone
with a circular base? Sketch the pattern at the right.

Map makers need to flatten a model of a sphere to create maps of the world. Because some curved
surfaces cannot be totally flattened without stretching and distorting them, some estimations and
approximations have to be made. Consider the model of the globe of the world and the "map" pattern
made from the globe shown below.

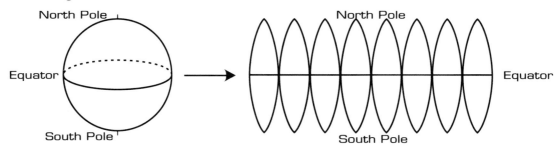

Where are land area measures approximately correct on this map? Explain. What happens to land
area measurements near the North Pole and the South Pole on this map? Explain. What are some
advantages and disadvantages of working with a map of this type?

INTERSECTIONS OF A PLANE WITH A CYLINDER, A CONE, OR A SPHERE

When you cut thin slices of an orange to float on the top of a fruit punch for a party, what shape are
the slices? If a plane intersects a sphere, what shape is the intersection?

Try to visualize the shape of the intersection of a plane and a cylinder; also the intersection of a plane
and a cone. Think of it as using a knife to cut a thin slice from a cake made in the form of a cylinder
(or a cone). What shape might the slice (cross section) be? Explain. The knife may pass through the
cake at different angles, so different-shaped cross sections (slices) can be formed.

In the chart below, check (or describe) the shape the of cross sections (slices) you might get by having
a plane intersect each figure. *Verify by slicing a clay model.*

Figure	Shape	Circle	Rectangle	Triangle	Other (describe)
Cylinder					
Cone					
Sphere					

Compare cylinders and cones. How are they alike? How are they different?

Compare spheres and circles. How are they alike? How are they different?

Find and report on examples of the use of cylinders, cones, spheres, and circles in your neighborhood.
Also cut out and organize a set of pictures from newspapers and magazines showing the use of these
geometric figures.

ACTIVITY 2C
MORE ABOUT SOLIDS

Decide whether or not each of these three-dimensional shapes satisfies Euler's formula for faces, vertices, and edges: $F + V = E + 2$.

If the diagrams are difficult to "read," make cardboard models to help count faces, vertices, and edges. Figures 3, 4, and 5 are hollow, that is, there is a hole through them.

1. F = ____
    V = ____
    E = ____

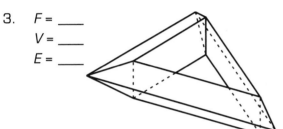

2. F = ____
    V = ____
    E = ____

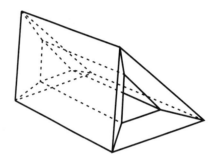

3. F = ____
    V = ____
    E = ____

4. F = ____
    V = ____
    E = ____

5. F = ____
    V = ____
    E = ____

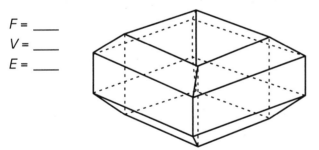

For which solids does the formula work? Is this the result you would have expected?

Do you see any other pattern? Consider the hollow shapes. Can you make a conjecture about this type of solid?

Challenge: Design another hollow shape and try out your conjecture.

ACTIVITY 3A
CONSTRUCTING ANGLES

1. When you turn on a flashlight, what do you see? What do you call this stream of light? Describe other times when you see streams of light. Frequently these streams of light are called rays. Describe a ray.

2. Cut out models of rays. Connect two rays with a paper fastener to form a model of an angle. Make another angle with two rays.

   Explore forming angles of different sizes by rotating the rays around the vertex (the paper fastener).

   Form the following angles (from a clock face) with your model angles and draw a sketch of each angle:

3:00 angle	6:00 angle
2:00 angle	8:00 angle
2:15 angle	10:00 angle

   Next to each angle, write a word used to describe its size.

   Are any of your angles congruent? Describe them. Create another pair of congruent angles with your model angles. Sketch the result.

3. Use a scrap of newspaper with no straight edges. Make a fold; fold again, matching up the straight edges. What kind of an angle have you created? Explain.

4. List examples around the classroom and in the real world of different types of angles.

5. Read and complete the following concept card:

These are adjacent angles (angles 1 and 2):

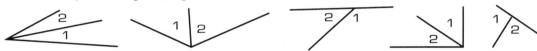

These are not adjacent angles (angles 1 and 2):

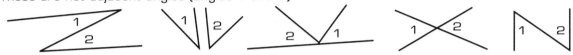

Which of these are adjacent angles (angles 1 and 2)?

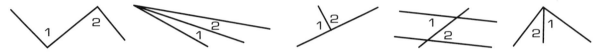

Using your model angles, create a pair of adjacent angles. Draw a sketch of your result.

Find and list pairs of adjacent angles in the figure on the right.

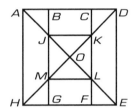

If you were to describe a pair of adjacent angles to a friend over the telephone, what would you say?

6. Optional: Make two model sets of vertical angles by cutting out four straight angles. Join each pair of straight angles with a paper fastener. Now place one model on top of the other and slide one above the other to create parallel lines cut by a transversal. Can you discover any pairs of congruent angles? Draw a sketch and list all pairs of congruent angles.

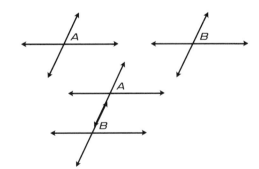

Change the position of your model angles. Are the pairs of angles still congruent?

What conjectures would you make about pairs of angles formed by parallel lines and a transversal?

ACTIVITY 3B
ANGLE MEASUREMENT

Here are three circles, each divided into a different number of equal wedges.

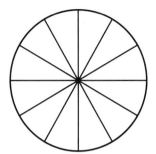 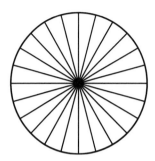 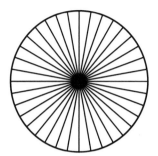

Circle 1: 12 A wedges   Circle 2: 24 B wedges   Circle 3: 36 C wedges

For each angle below, estimate how many wedges of each kind (A, B, or C) make up each angle. Check your estimate by tracing each angle, using tracing paper; overlay the tracing paper on each circle and count the number of wedges that fit in the angle.

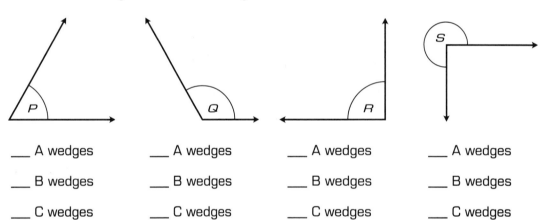

___ A wedges	___ A wedges	___ A wedges	___ A wedges
___ B wedges	___ B wedges	___ B wedges	___ B wedges
___ C wedges	___ C wedges	___ C wedges	___ C wedges

If there were another circle with 360 equal D wedges, estimate how many D wedges would fit in each angle. Explain your estimate.

Angle P: ___ D wedges   Angle Q: ___ D wedges   Angle R: ___ D wedges   Angle S: ___ D wedges

Is there another name for a D wedge?

Use or make a model of an equilateral triangle and measure its angles in terms of A, B, and C wedges. What is the sum of the wedges? What have you found? Will this always be true?

Draw a rectangle. Repeat the same measurements and questions as above.

ACTIVITY 4A
BUILDING TRIANGLES AND QUADRILATERALS

Why are tripods (three-legged supports) used by surveyors or camera enthusiasts in their work?

To begin to answer this question, let's construct some triangles. Use geostrips and paper fasteners.

1. Make two triangles and compare them with your neighbor's. How are the triangles alike? Describe. How are they different? Describe.

2. a. Make a triangle that has three congruent sides.

 b. Make a triangle that has exactly two congruent sides.

 c. Make a triangle that has no congruent sides.

 Triangles can be classified into three groups in terms of their sides:

 An **equilateral** triangle (from Latin: "equi" means *equal,* "latus" means *side*) has three congruent sides.

 An **isosceles** triangle (from Greek: "iso" means *equal,* "skelos" means *leg*) has two congruent sides.

 A **scalene** triangle (from Greek: "skalenos" means *uneven*) has no sides congruent.

 Draw sketches of your equilateral, isosceles, and scalene triangles.

 _____   _____   _____

 equilateral   isosceles   scalene

3. A specific triangle is usually named by using a different capital letter for each of the three vertices. For example, this triangle can be named *CAT* or *TAC* or *ACT*—the order of the letters does not matter.

 Label the vertices of the isosceles triangle you drew in question 2.

 Name it in three different ways: _____   _____   _____

4. a. Are all equilateral triangles congruent? Construct two different equilateral triangles, using two different-sized geostrips. Place one on top of the other—do they match? Compare yours with your neighbor's. If the triangles are not congruent, do any of their parts fit together? Describe.

 b. Use the angle models you constructed in the previous activity to examine the angles in one of your equilateral triangles. Are any of the angles the same size? Check your neighbor's equilateral triangles. What conjecture would you make about the angles in an equilateral triangle?

5. Are all isosceles triangles congruent? Try to make two different isosceles triangles. Compare yours with your neighbor's. Are any of the angles in one of your isosceles triangles the same size? Check the angles in one of your neighbor's isosceles triangles. What conjecture would you make about some of the angles in an isosceles triangle?

7. If you are given the following lengths for the three sides of a triangle, try to construct the triangle with geostrips or with a ruler:

   a. 16 cm, 7 cm, 10 cm   c. 13 cm, 7 cm, 16 cm

   b. 7 cm, 7 cm, 7 cm   d. 7 cm, 4 cm, 13 cm

   Use a ruler to create three other lengths and try to construct that triangle.

   Why was it not possible to create a triangle with some of the given lengths? From this investigation, make a conjecture about the relationship among the lengths of the three sides of a triangle. Check out your conjecture with a neighbor.

8. Is a triangle a "rigid" figure? That is, using one triangle you have constructed, can you shift it (without breaking it) in any way to change it into a different triangle? (Note: A different position on the table is not considered to be a different triangle.) Test out the different triangles that you have made. Are they "rigid"? What conjecture can you make about the rigidity of triangles from this activity?

   From this investigation, can you explain why tripods are used by surveyors and camera enthusiasts? Where do you see triangles used in your neighborhood?

9. If you built the outside frame of a bookcase in the form of a rectangle, would it need any extra supports to make it rigid? Explain. To investigate this question, let's construct some quadrilaterals.

   Select four congruent geostrips. Join the geostrips with paper fasteners to create the four-sided figure A (quadrilateral). What name would you give to figure A? Draw a sketch of figure A. Describe figure A.

   Is figure A "rigid"? That is, can you shift or flex it into a different-shaped plane quadrilateral? If you have been able to shift it into a new shape, what name would you give to figure B? Sketch figure B. Describe figure B. (On a separate sheet of paper, use the chart format shown at the right to sketch and describe your findings.)

   Using your angle models from a previous activity, examine the angles of your quadrilaterals. Describe your findings for figures A and B in your chart. Is one of your figures a square? How can you be sure?

Figure A: Rigid? Sketch: Name: Findings about angles:	Figure B: Rigid? Sketch: Name: Findings about angles:
Figure C:	Figure D:
Figure E:	Figure F:

10. Select two congruent geostrips and two other congruent geostrips of a different length. Join the strips by alternating the lengths and connect them to form a quadrilateral—call it figure C. Repeat question 9 and record the results on your chart.

11. Select two congruent geostrips and two other congruent geostrips of a different length. Join the strips by connecting the two shorter lengths together and the two longer lengths together. Connect these new strips to form a quadrilateral—call it figure D. Repeat question 9 and record the results on your chart.

12. Using geostrips, create two other quadrilaterals that have (a) exactly two congruent sides (figure E) and (b) no sides congruent (figure F). Investigate the properties of these figures and summarize your findings on the chart.

13. What would you do to make your bookcase more rigid? Explain. Does the quadrilateral become a rigid figure if you add one diagonal? Two diagonals?

ACTIVITY 4B
GEOMETRIC PRESUPPOSER INVESTIGATION OF TRIANGLES

1. Use the Draw, Triangle, Label, and Measure commands to gather data about the lengths of the three sides and the measures of the three angles of three different equilateral triangles. Record your results in the chart below.

   What observations can you make from the data you collected about the lengths of the sides and measures of the angles of the triangles? Do you notice any patterns or common characteristics? Describe.

2. Repeat question 1 for three isosceles triangles. Record the data on the chart below. Observations?

3. Repeat question 1 for three scalene triangles. Record the data on the chart below. Observations?

4. Repeat question 1 for three right triangles. Record the data on the chart below. Observations?

		Measure of—					
		side AB	side BC	side CA	$\angle BAC$	$\angle ABC$	$\angle BCA$
Equilateral	1						
	2						
	3						
Isosceles	1						
	2						
	3						
Scalene	1						
	2						
	3						
Right	1						
	2						
	3						

5. On the basis of the data above, what conjectures would you make—

   about equilateral triangles?

   about isosceles triangles?

   about scalene triangles?

   about right triangles?

   about the sides of any triangle?

ACTIVITY 5A
FIGURATE (POLYGONAL) NUMBERS

Examine the patterns and complete each table below.

1. Oblong numbers:
   G = number of dots

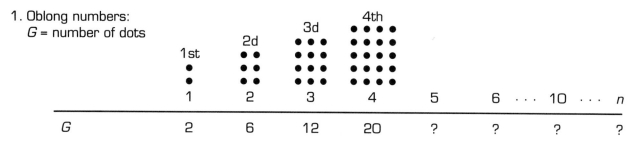

	1	2	3	4	5	6	··· 10 ···	n
G	2	6	12	20	?	?	?	?

How can you predict the next oblong number? What patterns can you find? Describe.

2. Triangular numbers:
   T = number of dots

	1	2	3	4	5	6	··· 10 ···	n
T	1	3	6	10	?	?	?	?

How can you predict the next triangular number? What patterns can you find? Describe.

3. Square numbers:
   S = number of dots

	1	2	3	4	5	6	··· 10 ···	n
S	1	4	9	16	?	?	?	?

How can you predict the next square number? What patterns can you find? Describe.

4. Can you find a relationship between the oblong and the triangular numbers? Describe it. How would you explain the relationship by using only the dot representations?

5. What relationships can you find between two consecutive triangular numbers and a square number? Describe. How would you explain these relationships by only using the dot representations?

6. Optional: Sometimes you will see fruit or cans in grocery stores piled high in the form of a pyramid as shown. The number of pieces of fruit or cans is sometimes called a *pyramidal number.*

   Pyramidal numbers:
   Y = number of dots

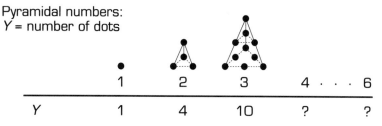

	1	2	3	4 ··· 6	
Y	1	4	10	?	?

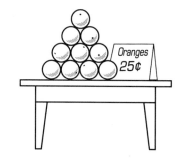

Oranges
25¢

What patterns can you find? Describe.

ACTIVITY 5B
DISCOVERING PATTERNS WITH LINES

Try to discover patterns in the following figures; describe the patterns.

1. Number of points on a line	Number of different line segments
2	1
3	3
4	
5	
6	
7	
.	
.	
.	
10	
.	
.	
.	
25	
.	
.	
.	
n	

Describe the pattern:

2. Number of sides	Number of diagonals
3	0
4	2
5	
6	
.	
.	
.	
15	
.	
.	
.	
n	

Describe the pattern:

3. How are the patterns alike? How are they different?

ACTIVITY 5C
DISCOVERING PATTERNS WITH TILES AND STICKS

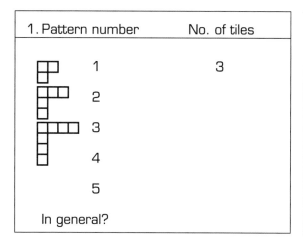

1. Pattern number	No. of tiles
1	3
2	
3	
4	
5	
In general?	

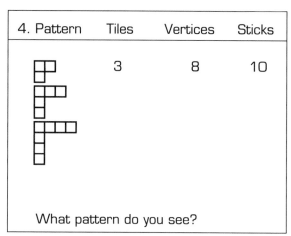

2. Pattern number	No. of sticks
1	10
2	
3	
4	
5	
In general?	

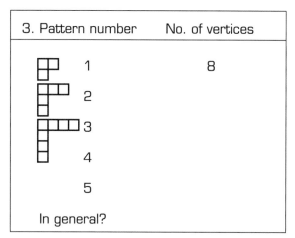

3. Pattern number	No. of vertices
1	8
2	
3	
4	
5	
In general?	

4. Pattern	Tiles	Vertices	Sticks
	3	8	10
What pattern do you see?			

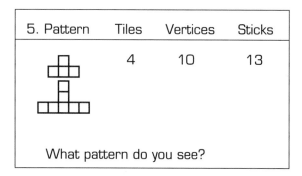

5. Pattern	Tiles	Vertices	Sticks
	4	10	13
What pattern do you see?			

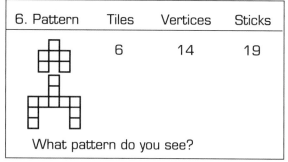

6. Pattern	Tiles	Vertices	Sticks
	6	14	19
What pattern do you see?			

7. With eight tiles, create a pattern to form a square with a hole in the middle. Record the number of vertices and the number of sticks in a table. Using twelve tiles, create a pattern to form a square with a square hole in the middle. Do the same with sixteen tiles. What patterns do you see? How is this pattern different from the other patterns?

ACTIVITY 5D
PATTERNS ON A GEOBOARD

1. On your geoboard, construct each of the following figures with one rubber band and record each result on dot paper:

   a. an acute triangle

   b. a right triangle

   c. a scalene triangle

   d. an isosceles triangle

   e. a scalene quadrilateral

   f. a rectangle with four congruent sides

   g. a parallelogram with four right angles

   h. a trapezoid with two congruent sides

   i. a pentagon

   j. a hexagon

   Check with your neighbors. Are different correct results possible? Explain.

2. In the diagrams below, points A, B, C, and D are called *boundary* points and points E, F, and G are called *interior* points.

   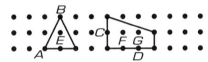

   Construct the following figures on your geoboard and record each result on dot paper:

   a. a triangle with no interior points and four boundary points

   b. a triangle with one interior point and six boundary points

   c. a quadrilateral with one interior point and eight boundary points

   d. a square with four interior points (How many boundary points does it have?)

   e. a quadrilateral with two interior points and only two sides parallel

   Check with your neighbors. Are different correct results possible? Explain.

3. Construct a triangle on your geoboard. Do not show it to your neighbor but give her or him careful instructions on how to create your triangle on her or his geoboard. When finished, compare your triangle with your neighbor's. Are they congruent? If they are not congruent, explain why. Now reverse roles. Let your neighbor construct a quadrilateral on a geoboard (without showing it to you) and then give you instructions to construct the same quadrilateral on your geoboard. Compare results. Are they congruent? If they are not congruent, explain why.

4. How many different-sized squares can you find on your geoboard? Record them on dot paper. (Hint: Be sure to turn your geoboard so that it looks like a diamond shape in order to find more different-sized squares.)

5. Place one rubber band in a vertical position on your geoboard to divide it in half. On one side of the rubber band, construct a scalene right triangle. Think of the rubber band as a mirror, and ask your neighbor to construct a scalene right triangle on the geoboard on the other side of the rubber band so that the new triangle is a reflection of your triangle. Do you agree with your neighbor's construction? Record your triangle and its reflection on dot paper.

6. Challenge: Can you construct an equilateral triangle on a geoboard that has its pegs arranged in a square grid pattern? Why or why not? (Check the length of the sides with a ruler.)

ACTIVITY 5E
PYTHAGOREAN THEOREM

1. On graph paper, create five right triangles with legs of the following lengths:

    a. 3 and 4   d. 6 and 8

    b. 5 and 12   e. 8 and 15

    c. 7 and 24

Find the length of the hypotenuses of each of these triangles (use a strip of graph paper) and record the data in the first three columns of the chart below:

	leg 1	leg 2	hyp		(leg 1)²	(leg 2)²	(hyp)²
a.	3	4					
b.	5	12					
c.							
d.							
e.							
f.	a	b	c				

Now complete the last three columns of the chart.

Do you see any patterns? Describe.

What conjecture would you make concerning the lengths of the three sides of a right triangle?

2. a. In the middle of a geoboard, create a small right isosceles triangle and construct a square on each side of the triangle. Record the result on dot paper. Is there a relationship among the areas of the three squares? Describe.

   b. Repeat the activity above on a geoboard, using a right triangle with legs of 1 and 2 units.

   c. From a set of tangram pieces, select the middle-sized right triangle. Now build squares on each side of the triangle using the following tangram pieces: two large triangles, two middle-sized triangles, and four small triangles. Is there a relationship among the areas of the three squares? Describe it.

   d. From the visual representation of the triangles below, what conjectures might you make about the relationship of $a^2 + b^2$ to c^2 for an acute triangle? For an obtuse triangle?

3. Real-world applications:

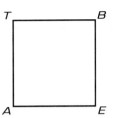

a. If two joggers want to go from *A* to *B* in a square-shaped open field, what possible paths could they take (without retracing any direction)? What is the length of the shortest path? What is the longest path? Explain.

b. Can a circular table top with diameter 2.7 meters long fit through a doorway 2.5 meters high and 1 meter wide? Why or why not?

c. How far up on a wall of a building will a 10-meter ladder reach if the foot of the ladder is 6 meters from the wall? Explain.

d. What is the length of the longest pole you could put in a rectangular storage room 12 units long, 9 units wide, and 8 units high? Explain.

4. Challenge:

• In the middle of a sheet of paper, draw a right triangle *ABC* (right angle at *C*) with legs of 1 unit.

   Using segment *BA* as a leg, draw a right triangle *ABD* (right angle at *A*) and leg *AD* equal to 1unit.

   Using segment *BD* as a leg, draw a right triangle *BDE* (right angle at *D*) and leg *DE* equal to 1 unit.

   Using segment *BE* as a leg, draw a right triangle *BEF* (right angle at *E*) and leg *EF* equal to 1 unit.

• Continue this process at least eight more times.

• What is the length of each hypotenuse? What patterns do you notice? Describe.

• If you continued this process twenty more times, what figure would you get? Make a sketch of the resulting figures.

ACTIVITY 6
TANGRAMS AND VISUALIZATION

1. Cut the tangram puzzle into the seven pieces.

2. Sort the pieces. Which belong together? Record your sort by making a sketch.

3. How are the five triangles alike? Different?

4. a. Put the two small triangles together so that one pair of sides of the two triangles fit together. Does this new shape match any other shape in the puzzle? Which?

   b. Repeat part (a) to make a different shape. Does this new shape match any other shape in the puzzle? Which?

   c. Repeat part (a) to make another shape. Does this new shape match any other shape in the puzzle? Which?

5. Repeat this activity by putting the two large triangles together (making one pair of sides fit together). What shapes do you get?

6. Put the three smaller triangles together to form these shapes:

   (a) a square

   (b) a rectangle that is not a square

   (c) a parallelogram that is not a rectangle

   (d) a trapezoid

   (e) a right triangle

   Sketch each result. What is the same about each figure formed in (a) through (e)?

7. Now use all seven pieces and repeat question 6. Sketch your results.
   For example: A cat

   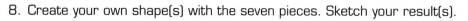

8. Create your own shape(s) with the seven pieces. Sketch your result(s).

9. a. If the puzzle were made of gold leaf and the smallest triangle cost $10, what would the whole puzzle cost? Explain how you found your answer.

   b. If the whole puzzle were worth $1, what would be the value of each piece? Explain how you found your answer.

line	perpendicular	acute
complementary	plane	congruent
skew	angle	ray
obtuse	segment	right
supplementary	intersecting	vertical
parallel	point	adjacent
prism	cone	quadrilateral
pyramid	sphere	edge
polyhedron	cube	face
cylinder	triangle	vertex
similar	circle	radius

♦ ♦ ♦ ♦ ♦ ♦ ♦ ♦

CLUSTER B
RELATIONSHIPS AMONG PROPERTIES OF SHAPES
INCLUDING ANGLE SUMS

Activity 8: Parallelogram and Triangular Grids

    a. Parallelogram Grid and Minideductions

    b. Triangular Grid: Reading the Grid

    c. Triangle Angle Sum

Activity 9: Polygon Angle Sum

Activity 10: Tessellations and Space-filling Forms

Activity 11: Family Trees and Angle Sums

Activity 12: Logo Investigation of Polygons

Activity 13: Properties of Quadrilaterals

    a. "Roots" of a Square

    b. Family Trees and Kites

    c. Properties of Quadrilaterals

    d. Geometric PreSupposer Investigation of Quadrilaterals

Activity 14: Creative Problem Solving with Shapes

    a. Creative Geometry Problem Solving with Yarn

    b. Shapes and Water in a Cube

OBJECTIVES OF CLUSTER B:

1. To recognize certain shapes in a grid, analyze components, and discover relationships by "reading the grid"

2. To give cogent arguments (minideductions) to establish conclusions from given and deduced information

3. To recognize that different, but equivalent, valid arguments are possible

4. To extend the concept of angle sum for triangles to n-sided polygons

5. To observe patterns and make conjectures (i.e., use inductive reasoning) relating to interior and exterior angle sums for polygons

6. To observe, define, and create in a plane tessellations formed by various types of polygons

7. To give logical arguments to justify why certain polygons do or do not tessellate

8. To create Escher type of tessellations

9. To investigate applications of three-dimensional tessellations as in the design of various types of packaging containers

10. To investigate construction of polygons using Logo

11. To discover and explain subclass relationships in the quadrilateral family and to diagram these relationships in a family tree or Venn diagram format

12. To introduce (by a concept card approach) a new quadrilateral (a kite) to the family and to determine its relationship to the rest of the quadrilateral family

13. To investigate properties of diagonals of quadrilaterals

14. To give students experience in developing definitions in geometry

15. To engage students in problem-solving situations that require visualization skills and cooperative group effort

TEACHING NOTES FOR CLUSTER B:

This cluster of activities focuses on student investigation and development of the relationships of properties of shapes and angle sums in the spirit of the van Hiele model of the levels of thinking in geometry.

Activity 8: Parallelogram and Triangular Grids

Materials: Copies of Activity Sheets 8a, 8b, and 8c for students; colored pencils or crayons; different triangular grids

The grids on the activity sheets are formed by sets of parallel lines: the parallelogram grid has two sets of parallel lines, whereas the triangular grid has three sets. To give students some insight into how different grids can be constructed from parallelograms or triangles, students or the teacher can demonstrate how a given parallelogram or triangle tessellates a plane to form a grid. (A small quantity of each different type of congruent parallelogram or congruent triangle will be needed.) Examples of grids seen and used in the real world should be discussed.

Activity 8a: Parallelogram Grid and Minideductions

Before doing this activity students need to be familiar with, and have had some experience in identifying, alternate interior angles ("saw") and corresponding angles ("ladder"). The purpose of this activity is to have students identify certain angles (Level 0), see connections (Level 1), and deduce conclusions (Level 2). Part a involves recognizing and applying this principle: If lines are parallel, alternate interior/corresponding angles are congruent. Part b requires a two-step argument involving the transitive principle (e.g., angle a = angle x, angle x = angle c, hence angle a = angle c). Part c also requires a minideduction using the transitive principle. Have the students verbalize (and appreciate) the important principle that was "proved" or deduced—the opposite angles of a parallelogram are congruent. The students need to realize that certain conclusions about angles or line segments can be established by deduction without resorting to measuring them. (It is of interest to note that at this stage most middle school students do not fully appreciate the power of deduction and will want to measure the angles, in their words, "just to be sure.") For additional information on the van Hiele levels, see Crawley (1987) and Shaughnessy and Burger (1985).

Activity 8b: Triangular Grid: Reading the Grid

Have students discover as many geometry ideas as possible in the grids. They can "read from the grid" such ideas as the following (fig. 18):

- Alternate interior ("saw") angles, corresponding ("ladder") angles, congruent angles (by coloring angles on the grid)
- Parallelograms of different shapes; congruence of opposite angles of a parallelogram
- Congruent triangles; different shapes with equal areas
- Trapezoids, hexagons; similar triangles

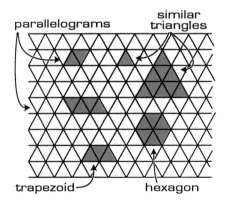

parallelograms   similar triangles

trapezoid   hexagon

Fig. 18

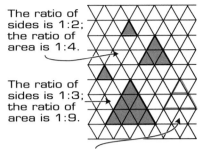

The ratio of sides is 1:2; the ratio of area is 1:4.

The ratio of sides is 1:3; the ratio of area is 1:9.

The line joining midpoints of 2 sides of a △ = 1/2 the third side.

Fig. 19

Raise questions and encourage students to "read the grid"—to make observations and discoveries and to formulate conjectures that they can verify by examples on the grid. Some possible conjectures follow (fig. 19):

- The line joining the midpoints of two sides of a triangle is parallel to the third side and has a length equal to one-half the length of the third side.
- The areas of two similar triangles are to each other as the squares of the corresponding sides.

Activity 8c: Triangle Angle Sum

Raise questions and encourage students to "read the grid"—to make observations and formulate conjectures that they can verify by examples from the grid. In particular, they should note the following (fig. 20):

- The sum of the measures of the angles of a triangle is equal to the measure of a straight angle.
- The measure of an exterior angle of a triangle is equal to the sum of the measures of the two opposite interior angles.

"Reading from the grid" permits the students to discover and investigate all the relationships above. Students should explore and verify these relationships on several different types of triangular grids.

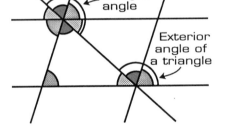

Straight angle

Exterior angle of a triangle

The "reading from the grid" approach (to establish the angle sum for a triangle) is an important tool and lays the groundwork for a more formal approach in the later study of geometry in high school. It supplements the traditional approaches of (1) tearing off the angles of the triangle to form a straight angle, (2) folding the angles of the triangles together to form a straight angle, and (3) finding the measures of the angles with a protractor. Another approach to finding the angle sum simply by using a pencil is described in Activity 9.

Activity 9: Polygon Angle Sum

Materials: Copies of Activity Sheet 9 for students

Have students in cooperative groups draw a set of polygons with 4, 5, 6, 8, and 10 sides (see Appendix). Students should discuss and plan how to find the interior angle sum for these polygons. Groups should share ideas. One plan might be based on using the angle sum of a triangle. Data can be summarized in this chart, patterns noted, and conjectures made.

Students can also be challenged to find the sum of the measures of the angles of a polygon by using just a pencil. After discussion and experimentation, students should find the following procedure of interest (see fig. 21):

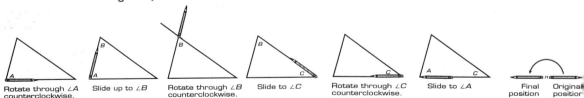

Rotate through ∠A counterclockwise. | Slide up to ∠B | Rotate through ∠B counterclockwise. | Slide to ∠C | Rotate through ∠C counterclockwise. | Slide to ∠A | Final position | Original position

Fig. 21

Through how many degrees did the pencil rotate? Extend the procedure to find the sum of the measures of the interior angles of quadrilaterals, pentagons, and hexagons.

Extension: The activity can be extended to consider the sum of the measures of the exterior angles (one at each vertex) of polygons. The moving pencil approach is very useful here.

Activity 10: Tessellations and Space-filling Forms

Materials: Envelopes containing sets of congruent polygons (prepared from the template in the Appendix); tracing paper; colored crayons; photographs or posters showing regular and semiregular tessellations; a variety of boxes used by manufacturers for packaging their products; copies of Activity Sheet 10 for students

Tessellations (tilings) have many real-world applications (e.g., floor covering, art design, quilts, packaging). Have students look at tiling patterns in the classroom or in photographs to gain an intuitve understanding of the meaning of the word *tessellation* (i.e., when polygons are fitted together to fill a plane with no overlaps or gaps, the pattern is called a tessellation). Tessellation patterns can be made from one shape or more than one shape. In the initial investigation, one shape should be used.

To organize this laboratory activity, prepare in advance small envelopes of sets of conguent tiles (one type of polygon in each envelope). There should be separate envelopes for each type of triangle, each type of quadrilateral (including kite, regular, irregular, and concave), and some types of regular polygons (pentagon, hexagon, octagon, dodecagon). Each envelope should contain approximately twelve congruent tiles of one shape. Each group of students should receive several envelopes so they have a variety of different shapes to try to tessellate. For the first activity, only envelopes containing triangles or quadrilaterals should be distributed.

Students in each group should work together to see whether the tiles (shapes) in each envelope can be placed together to form a tessellation. Be sure the groups extend their *patterns* sufficiently so they are sure their pattern can be extended to cover a large portion of a plane. Each group's tilings should be displayed on the desks so that groups can briefly move to view the different tessellations.

Have students draw a variety of triangles and quadrilaterals on a piece of paper. Ask, Can you use your shapes to make a tiling pattern? Students should then use tracing paper to create tessellations to justify their conclusions. Discussion should include these questions: Which triangles can tessellate a plane? Which quadrilaterals can tessellate a plane? This discussion should lead to generalizations and conjectures.

The question of why all quadrilaterals and all triangles tessellate should be explored. Have students color in the angles of several copies of an irregular quadrilateral with four different colors in the same way and then create a tiling. What do they observe around each vertex in the tiling? They should note that the corners of four quadrilaterals always meet at a point; each quadrilateral presents a different corner (angle), so the sum is 360 degrees—thus there is no gap and no overlap.

Now the envelopes containing sets of regular polygons should be distributed to each group. The term "regular" polygon should be reviewed (a regular polygon is both equilateral and equiangular). Discussion should focus on the question, Which regular polygons tessellate? Groups should share their findings. Discussion should focus on why certain regular polygons tessellate and others do not. Have students determine the measure of an interior angle of each regular polygon and record the results as in figure 22. Students should notice from the data that there are only three regular tessellations.

Polygon	Meas. of int. ∠	No. of polygons around point	Gap or overlap
Triangle	60°	6	No gap
Square	90°	4	No gap
Pentagon	108°	3	Gap
Hexagon	120°	3	No gap
Octagon	135°	2	Gap
Decagon	144°	2	Gap
Dodecagon	150°	2	Gap

Fig. 22

Some students may note that different tessellations could be made with some of the regular polygons if they could use two shapes. Students should explore making some semiregular tessellations with a pair of regular polygons. This should then lead to discussions of semiregular tessellations; posters or photographs of these are useful displays. Students should also explore tessellating with nonregular pentagons, hexagons, and other shapes. For additional activities, see Bezuszka, Kenney, and Silvey (1977), Giganti and Citadino (1990), and O'Daffer and Clemens (1992).

Extension: Some Escher tessellations might be shown. Demonstrate how a simple Esher type of tessellation can be constructed; see Serra (1989, pp. 324–37).

Extension: Consider the question of how manufacturers might design containers for packaging their products without waste of space. Use a collection of commercial product containers (e.g., cereal boxes—rectangular prisms; boxes of straws—square prisms; chocolate or cosmetic boxes—triangular prisms; light bulb containers—hexagonal prisms). Have students note how each type might fit together for shipping. Are there gaps? Discuss how this concept is related to their work with tessellations.

Activity 11: Family Trees and Angle Sums

Materials: Copies of Activity Sheet 11 for students

This activity is designed to have students reflect on the logical ordering of relationships through the use of a "family tree" format.

Activity 12: Logo Investigation of Polygons

Materials: Copies of Activity Sheet 12 for students; Logo software; computers (For other geometric investigative software, see The Geometer's Sketchpad.)

Students should have had a brief experience with Logo and Logo primitive commands—FORWARD (FD), BACK (BK), RIGHT (RT), LEFT (LT), SHOW TURTLE (ST)—before doing this activity. They should work at the computers in pairs and should have some background knowledge of polygons and angles. For additional Logo activities, see Battista and Clements (1990), Kenney and Bezuszka (1989), Moore (1984), and Niess (1988).

Activity 13: Properties of Quadrilaterals

Materials: Copies of Activity Sheets 13a-13d for students; moveable models of quadrilaterals made with geostrips (see Appendix), D-Stix, or straws and pipe cleaners; Geometric PreSupposer software and computers (for part 13d).

This activity has four parts: parts a, b, and c are sequential and part d is optional. Students find Activity 13a enjoyable and the follow-up activities involving family trees and Venn diagrams challenging and thought provoking. In Activity 13c, subclass relationships among quadrilaterals are explored, and properties of diagonals of various quadrilaterals are investigated. This investigation should be done with moveable models or with cut-out models that can be folded and measured. If computers are available for Activity Sheet 13d, the Geometric PreSupposer is particularly well suited for this investigation.

Activity 14: Creative Problem Solving with Shapes

Materials: Copies of Activity Sheets 14a and 14b for students; lengths of heavy yarn (approximately 4 meters) for each group; one liter box with cover for each group; water; food coloring

These are cooperative learning activities. Each group should have four or five students. In Activity 14a, the groups need enough space to stand and move around.

Students enjoy and are challenged by these tasks. Be prepared for lots of activity. Groups may challenge and even compete with each other to complete the tasks and create new ones. Many "what if" questions arise in the discussion.

EVALUATION NOTES FOR ACTIVITIES 8–14

Reasons for evaluation:

- To evaluate students' grasp of concepts and to discover any misconceptions needing to be corrected or clarified

- To evaluate students' visualization skills

- To assess students' higher-order thinking skills and van Hiele level of thinking

- To assess students' comprehension of basic concepts and their ability to demonstrate and explain the interrelationships among these concepts using "family tree" or Venn diagram formats

- To build students' confidence in using logical arguments to justify conclusions

- To encourage students' investigations and explorations that may lead to new conjectures

- To stimulate creative problem solving in cooperative groups

- To extend mathematics learning beyond the classroom

Activities 8–14

Teacher assignments for student portfolios and activities:

1. Complete these "journal writes":

    a. Write informal arguments (proofs or minideductions) for several given problems (similar to those presented in Activities 8a, 8b, 8c). Justify (explain why) each step of your argument is true.

    b. Write a letter to a friend (who knows nothing about grids) and describe the grids you have been using; explain what properties of triangles you have discovered, made conjectures about, and verified by "reading the grids"; in particular, explain how it is possible to deduce the angle sum for a triangle by using a triangular grid.

2. Complete Activity Sheets 13a–13c:

    a. Create a concept card for "kites." Have a neighbor review your concept card and together discuss possible modifications. Write a summary of your discussion.

    b. Create a family tree or a Venn diagram to show the interrelationships that exist in the family of quadrilaterals. Write out a brief statement to explain your tree or diagram.

c. Explain how knowing all the properties of a parallelogram helps you know specific properties of some other quadrilaterals.

d. Describe examples of the use of quadrilaterals in real-world settings and explain why you think some types of quadrilaterals are used more often than others.

3. Complete creative problem-solving activities as presented in Activity 14; explain your strategies and solutions.

4. Prepare a laboratory report of (a) an investigation you did on the construction of regular polygons using Logo or (b) an investigation you completed on the properties of diagonals of quadrilaterals using the Geometric PreSupposer. Indicate the problem investigated, the shapes examined, the observations made, the data collected, and the conjectures made. Include verifications, unanswered questions, and possible extensions of the problem.

5. Find and organize a set of photographs from magazines, catalogs, or newspapers that show the use of tessellations in the real world. Briefly describe your collection, including the mathematical ideas involved.

6. Extension: For a wide variety of geometry and spatial visualization actvities designed to foster higher-level thinking, see Mathematics Resource Project (1978).

Evaluation of portfolios and activities:

1. "Journal writes": Monitor students' ability to identify "saw" and "ladder" angles that are congruent, to use appropriate vocabulary, and to use this information in completing problems requiring minideductions. Each step of these informal arguments should be justified by the student. (Students might exchange their "journal writes" involving minideductions with classmates and have them evaluate each other's arguments.) Students' higher-order thinking can be evaluated partially by their ability to create concept cards, to write out cogent arguments (van Hiele Level 2 thinking) to explain angle sums of polygons, and to create and explain family trees or Venn diagrams showing interrelationships of shapes and their properties.

2. The laboratory report can be assessed on the basis of the plan and the thoroughness of the investigation in light of the problem posed, the logical thinking and the analysis of the results obtained, the comprehensiveness of the report, and the significance of the questions and extensions being considered. The laboratory report gives some measure of the student's ability to plan an investigation of a problem, take risks, and make conjectures.

3. Problem-solving activities: Circulating among student groups, listening to student discussion, comments, and questions, and noting responses to suggestions for alternative solutions or "what if" questions give insight into students' ability to plan approaches to problem exploration and into their confidence and ability to explain and verify solutions.

ACTIVITY 8A
PARALLELOGRAM GRID AND MINIDEDUCTIONS

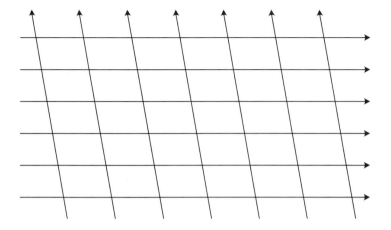

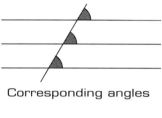

Corresponding angles

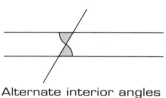

Alternate interior angles

This grid is formed by sets of parallel lines.

What shapes do you see in the grid?

Using one color, color in one set of corresponding angles in the grid. Are the angles congruent? Why or why not?

Using a different color, color in a different set of corresponding angles. Are the angles congruent? Why or why not?

In the grid, now use a third color to color in a set of alternate interior angles. Are the angles congruent? Why or why not?

Using a fourth color, color in another set of alternate interior angles. Are the angles congruent? Why or why not?

The following diagrams have been taken out of parallelogram grids. Examine each diagram and explain how to obtain the conclusion from the given information.

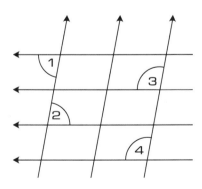

(a) Show angle 1 ≅ angle 2;
angle 3 ≅ angle 4

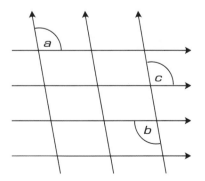

(b) Show angle *a* ≅ angle *c*;
angle *a* ≅ angle *b*

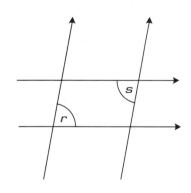

(c) Show angle *r* ≅ angle *s*

ACTIVITY 8B
TRIANGULAR GRID: READING THE GRID

This grid is formed by sets of parallel lines.

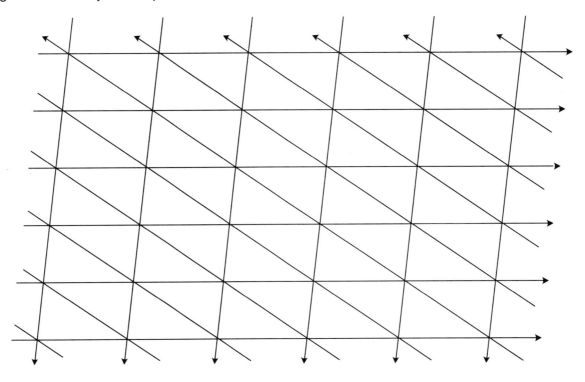

1. What geometry shapes and ideas do you see in the grid? List them.

2. Did you find any trapezoids? Outline one. Any hexagons? Outline one. Any different-shaped parallelograms? Outline a pair. Do they have equal areas? Why or why not?

3. Did you find any similar triangles? Outline a pair. What is the ratio of their sides? What is the ratio of their areas? Find another pair of similar triangles whose sides are in the ratio of 1:3. Outline them. What is the ratio of their areas? If the ratio of the sides of two similar triangles is 1:4, what would you predict for the ratio of their areas? What conjecture might you make concerning the ratio of the areas of similar triangles?

4. On the grid, outline a triangle that has a line joining the midpoints of two of its sides. (The line is called a midline.) Compare the length of the midline to the length of the third side of the triangle. What do you notice?

Outline two other different triangles on the grid; draw midlines and repeat the same comparison as above. Are the comparisons numerically the same? A triangle has three midlines. Try drawing in a different midline in one of your triangles and make the same comparison. Do you get the same result? What conjecture might you make about a midline of a triangle?

ACTIVITY 8C
TRIANGLE ANGLE SUM

This grid is formed by three sets of parallel lines.

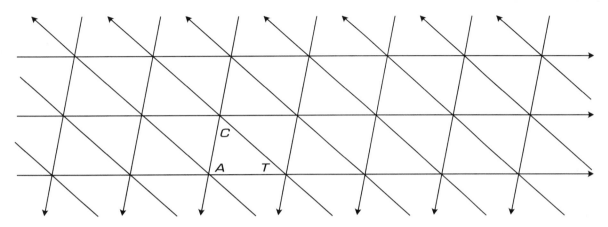

1. Outline triangle *CAT* on this grid. Choose three different color crayons. With the first color, color in angle *C* and all the angles near points *C*, *A*, and *T* that are congruent to angle *C*. With the second color, color in angle *A* and all the angles near points *C*, *A*, and *T* that are congruent to angle *A*. With the third color, color in angle *T* and all the angles near points *C*, *A*, and *T* that are congruent to angle *T*.

2. Now study the result. What do you observe about the angles around *C*? Around *A*? Around *T*? Find a straight angle in the colored diagram. What colors are the angles that make up the straight angle? Find another straight angle in your colored diagram. What colors are the angles that make up this straight angle? Repeat this process with another straight angle. What colors did you find?

   What are the colors of the three angles of the original triangle?

   What conjecture can you make about the angle sum of triangle *CAT*?

   Do you think this conjecture is true for all triangles? Investigate this conjecture on a different triangular grid.

3. In the diagram, angle *CTS* is called an exterior angle of triangle *CAT*. An exterior angle is formed by one side of a triangle with the extension of an adjacent side. Is angle *ACE* an exterior angle of triangle *CAT*? Why? Name another exterior angle.

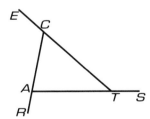

   Examine the size of an exterior angle in your colored diagram above in relation to interior angles of the triangle. Do this for several exterior angles. Do you notice any pattern? What conjecture might you make?

   Justify your conclusion.

ACTIVITY 9
POLYGON ANGLE SUM

Draw sketches of each of the polygons and complete the information in the chart below.

Polygon	Sketch	No. of sides	No. of diagonals from 1 vertex	No. of triangles	Interior angle sum	Exterior angle sum
triangle	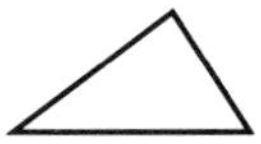	3	0	1	1 straight angle, or 180°	
quadrilateral		4	1	2	2(180°) = 360°	
pentagon						
hexagon						
octagon						
decagon						
dodecagon						
n-gon		n				

What conjecture can you make about the sum of the measures of the interior angles of a polygon of n sides?

Challenge: Can you find the sum of the measures of the angles in a polygon just by moving (rotating) a pencil to measure the angles?

ACTIVITY 10
TESSELLATIONS AND SPACE-FILLING FORMS

1. Can you find any tiling patterns in or near your classroom? Describe them. Where else have you seen tiling patterns? Describe them to your neighbor.

   If tiles are used to cover a plane surface with no overlap and no gaps, the tiling is called a *tessellation*.

2. Take the envelope for your group and investigate whether the same-shaped tiles in the envelope can be placed together to form a tessellation. Each group should report its results to the class.

3. a. In your group, draw examples of an acute scalene triangle, a right scalene triangle, an obtuse scalene triangle, an equilateral triangle, and an isosceles triangle. Answer this question: Which of your triangles can be used to make a tiling pattern? Use tracing paper to try to create a tessellation with each of your triangles.

   b. In your group, draw different types of quadrilaterals. Which of your quadrilaterals can be used to tessellate a plane surface? Verify your conclusions by trying to create a tessellation with each of your quadrilaterals.

   c. What conjectures would you make as a result of your investigations in parts a and b?

4. Take one of your irregular quadrilaterals and color in the four angles with four different colors. Now try to create a tiling with several copies of your shape. Were you successful? If not, try again by placing the quadrilaterals so that four angles—one angle of each color—come together at each vertex and the sides match. What is the sum of the measures of these four angles? Explain why there should be no gap or overlap in this tiling.

5. Take the envelope of regular polygons for your group and investigate which regular polygons tessellate. Find the measure of each interior angle of the regular polygons in your set. How many of the polygons of the same shape can you place around a point without an overlap? Record your findings in the chart below.

Polygon	Sketch	Measure of interior angle	How many polygons around a point?	Gap or overlap?
triangle	△	60°	6	No gap
square	☐			
pentagon				
hexagon				
octagon				
decagon				
dodecagon				

What conjectures can you make as a result of this investigation of regular polygons?

6. Extension: Why do manufacturers make specially designed containers for packaging their products? How might the idea of tessellation be important in their designs?

ACTIVITY 11
FAMILY TREES AND ANGLE SUMS

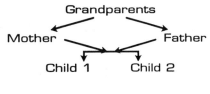

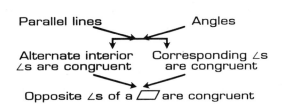

1. Examine the "family tree" at the left. Can you find the "ancestors" of the children? Describe them.

2. Here is a "family tree" in geometry. What are the "ancestors" of a quadrilateral?

3. Sometimes we build a family tree to show a logical ordering among relationships. For an example, examine the tree at the left.

   Explain this tree to your neighbor.

4. Let's try to build a family tree to show a logical ordering of relationships that led to our conjectures about—

   (a) the sum of the measures of the interior angles of a triangle;

   (b) tessellations of triangles and quadrilaterals.

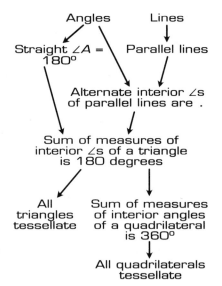

   (1) Examine the "tree" at the right; explain the ancestors of the sum for a triangle to a neighbor. (Think of the triangular grid.)

   (2) Ask your neighbor to explain the ancestors of the angle sum for a quadrilateral.

   (3) Why does "all triangles tessellate" have the angle sum for a triangle as an ancestor?

   (4) What conjecture would have the angle sum for a quadrilateral as an ancestor?

   (5) To the tree, add branches that would lead to the conjecture that some regular polygons do not tessellate.

5. Challenge: Try to build some other geometry family trees. For example: "The measure of an exterior angle of a triangle is equal to the sum of the two nonadjacent interior angles." What are its ancestors?

ACTIVITY 12
LOGO INVESTIGATION OF POLYGONS

1. Below is a set of commands you might give to the Logo turtle. Read the list of commands and then sketch what you think the turtle will draw.

ST	Sketch:
FD 60	
RT 90	
FD 60	
RT 90	
FD 60	
RT 90	
FD 60	
RT 90	

   Now type in these commands on your computer and watch what the turtle does at each step. Notice in particular how the turtle forms an angle. What name would you give to the shape the turtle has drawn? What properties does your shape have? Did the turtle use these properties as it drew the shape? Explain how.

2. Now think about an equilateral triangle; visualize it and draw a sketch of it. Think about the properties of an equilateral triangle. Write a set of commands to have the turtle draw what you have sketched. Did the turtle draw an equilateral triangle? Are the sides and angles correct? If not, what instructions should you change? Have the turtle follow these changes. Did it draw an equilateral triangle now?

3. One student gave the turtle a set of commands to draw an equilateral triangle and this is what the turtle drew.

   What is wrong with the student's commands?

   Notice how the turtle forms the angles.

   How would you change the commands so an equilateral triangle is drawn by the turtle?

4. Think about a regular pentagon. What are its properties? Sketch one. Now write a set of commands to have the turtle draw what you have sketched. Was the turtle successful? If not, try again.

5. Think about a regular hexagon; sketch one. Write a set of commands to have the turtle draw a regular hexagon. Was the turtle successful? If not, try again.

6. For questions 1–5, describe which angle of the polygon the turtle created at each vertex; that is, was it an interior angle? If not, describe the angle. What was the sum of these angles for—

   A square?　　　An equilateral triangle?　　　A pentagon?　　　A hexagon?

   On the basis of this data, what conjecture would you make about the sum of the measures of these angles (describe the angles) for regular polygons?

7. Extension: Investigate to see if this conjecture is true if the polygon is not regular. What turtle commands would you give to create an isosceles triangle? A scalene triangle? A rectangle? A parallelogram that is not a rectangle? Any quadrilateral? Any pentagon?

My ancestors go back to the beginnings of the Euclidean plane to a family of POLYGONS. There, my great-great-grandfather, the QUADRILATERAL, was born. The quadrilateral had a dream of symmetry.

The next stage of evolution occurred. The outcast of the family, with one pair of sides parallel, was called a TRAPEZOID. At the same time, my great-grandfather, the PARALLELOGRAM, was born. He was a sight to behold with rotational symmetry and both pairs of sides parallel.

Great-grandfather was an adventurous soul who wanted to see the new world. On the rough voyage over, he was wrecked and tangled and became a RECTANGLE.

Meanwhile, another parallelogram was caught by a band of equilaterals, and they changed its shape from this ⬜ to this ⬦ .

It became a RHOMBUS.

So my mother was a Rhombus and my father was a Rectangle. I took the best qualities from each—my father's righteousness and my mother's equality. As you know, I turned out to be a real **square**...and we all lived diagonally ever after.

In light of the above tale, complete this **"family tree"** for quadrilaterals.

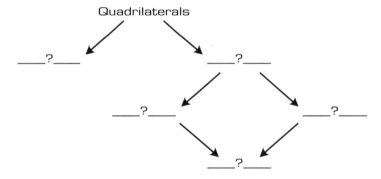

If you started drawing a Venn diagram to show the relationships in the quadrilateral family, how would you complete it?

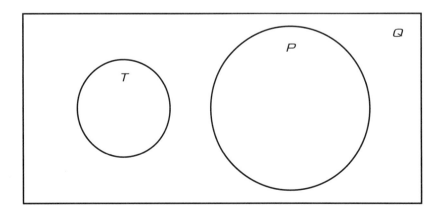

ACTIVITY 13B
FAMILY TREES AND KITES

1. Create a concept card for a KITE—a quadrilateral with two pairs of adjacent sides congruent. Here is the *beginning:*

   These are *kites:*

   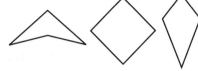

   These are *not* kites:

   Which of these are kites?

   Describe a kite.

2. Modify the Venn diagram and the family tree from Activity 13a to include the kite.

3. A different family tree (The arrow → means "is a special.")

   Select names from the following list to fill in the blanks that complete the family tree correctly:
   rhombus, square, kite, rectangle, trapezoid

   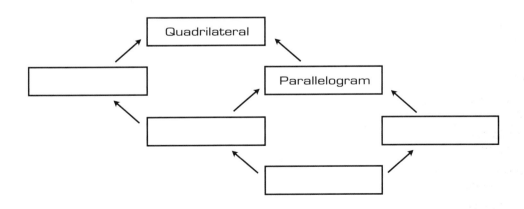

ACTIVITY 13C
PROPERTIES OF QUADRILATERALS

Select the figures that satisfy each of the sets of properties below and state their names.

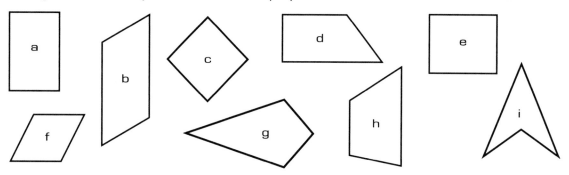

Has 4 sides. Opposite sides are congruent. Opposite sides are parallel. Opposite angles are congruent. Figures:_____ Name:_____	Has 4 sides. Only two sides are parallel. Figures:_____ Name:_____
Has 4 sides. All sides are congruent. Opposite sides are parallel. All angles are right angles. Figures:_____ Name:_____	Has 4 sides. Has two pairs of congruent adjacent sides. Figures:_____ Name:_____
Has 4 sides. Opposite sides are congruent. Opposite sides are parallel. All angles are right angles. Figures:_____ Name:_____	Has 4 sides. All sides are congruent. Opposite sides are parallel. Opposite angles are congruent. Figures:_____ Name:_____

Properties	Parallelogram	Rectangle	Rhombus	Square	Trapezoid	Kite
Diagonals bisect each other.						
Diagonals are congruent.						
Diagonals are perpendicular.						
Diagonals bisect vertex angles.						
One diagonal forms two ≅ triangles.						
Diagonals form four ≅ triangles.						

ACTIVITY 13D
GEOMETRIC PRESUPPOSER INVESTIGATION OF QUADRILATERALS

1. Use the Geometric PreSupposer to discover all the properties of the diagonals of each member of the quadrilateral family. Develop a plan for your investigation. Then list each property you investigated, the quadrilaterals you considered, and the data you collected. Summarize your observations and conclusions. Write this up in the form of a laboratory report. Include in the report the conjectures you are making about the diagonals of each member of the quadrilateral family as a result of your investigation, with brief explanations; also include any unanswered questions and some extensions of the problem that might be considered.

For example: Are diagonals ≅?   Do diagonals bisect each other?

trapezoid

parallelogram

2. Looking back: You know certain relationships exist among the members of the quadrilateral family. On the basis of that knowlege, do you think that all the data you collected were necessary? Are there parts of this investigation you could have omitted? Have you considered all possibilities? Explain your answers.

3. Extension: Using the Geometric PreSupposer, investigate what type of figure you might obtain by connecting, in order, the midpoints of the sides of a quadrilateral. Choose any quadrilateral; find and connect, in order, the midpoints of the four sides. What are the properties of the shape formed by joining the midpoints?

Repeat the investigation with several different types of quadrilaterals. What figure is formed if the original quadrilateral is a square? A rectangle? A parallelogram? A rhombus? A kite?

What conjectures would you make on the basis of the results of your investigation?

ACTIVITY 14A
CREATIVE GEOMETRY PROBLEM SOLVING WITH YARN

Your group of four to five students should have a loop of heavy yarn approximately four meters long.

The only "rule" in this activity is that each member of your group must have *both* hands touching the yarn at *all* times.

Your group's challenge is to make geometric figures with the yarn. Such figures might include—

- an isosceles triangle;
- a square;
- a parallelogram that is not a rhombus;
- a trapezoid;
- a kite (consider several solutions);
- a regular hexagon.

You must visualize and work cooperatively in thinking how to approach each challenge. Questions should be raised: How do you know your figure is a square? How can you be sure the sides are parallel?

Now use your loop of yarn to create more complex configurations including—

- three equilateral triangles;
- four congruent squares;
- three parallelograms that are not rectangles.

Now that you are experts, create a problem to challenge another group.

Extra challenge: Divide a regular hexagon into—

- 3 identical parts so each part is a rhombus;
- 4 identical parts so each part is a trapezoid;
- 6 identical parts so each part is a kite.

Adapted from "Creative Problem Solving and Red Yarn" (Wilmot 1985)

ACTIVITY 14B
SHAPES AND WATER IN A CUBE

1. Your group should have a liter box containing some colored water (use food coloring); the approximate depth of the water should be 4 centimeters. A container with additional water should be available for use if necessary.

2. Your group should discuss what is meant by a "cross section," in particular, a plane polygon cross section made by the top surface of the water in the liter box. For example, when the liter box sits flat on the table, the polygon cross section formed by the top surface of the water is a square. If the box is tilted slightly, the shape of the polygon cross section changes.

3. Challenge: Your group should position, if possible, the liter box so that the polygon cross section made by the top surface of the water has the following shapes:

   - A square
   - A rectangle that is not a square
   - A parallelogram that is not a rectangle
   - A trapezoid
   - An isosceles triangle
   - An equilateral triangle
   - A pentagon
   - A hexagon
   - An octagon
   - Other (student choices)

   Is it possible to create all the figures above with water in the liter box?

   If not, explain why particular shapes are impossible to create with water in a liter box.

CLUSTER C
TRANSFORMATION GEOMETRY

Activity 15: Mira (Reflecta) Activities

Activity 16: Slides, Flips, and Turns

Activity 17: Symmetry

Activity 18: Exploring Symmetry with Computer Software

> a. Exploring Symmetry with Logo

> b. Exploring Reflections (Flips) with the Geometric PreSupposer

Activity 19: Transformations and Coordinates

OBJECTIVES OF CLUSTER C:

1. To examine the concepts of transformation geometry in multiple embodiments (e.g., Mira, real-world applications, geoboard, dot paper, coordinate plane, computer technology)

2. To develop students' visual skills, reinforce understanding of basic geometric concepts, and develop higher-order thinking skills

3. To investigate the use of the Mira as a tool for doing basic geometric constructions; to compare paper folding with the use of the Mira (Reflecta)

4. To explore the motions of slides (translations), flips (reflections), and turns (rotations) in different settings using various materials and to make conjectures on the basis of these explorations

5. To examine concepts of symmetry and to sort and classify shapes on the basis of symmetry

6. To investigate transformation geometry concepts using Logo and the Geometric PreSupposer

7. To extend the notions of motion geometry to a coordinate plane setting and to discover patterns and make generalizations and conjectures in this setting

TEACHING NOTES FOR CLUSTER C:

Activity 15: Mira (Reflecta) Activities

Materials: Wax paper, copies of Activity Sheet 15 for students; Miras (Reflectas)

The Mira (Reflecta) is an excellent tool for doing all the basic geometry constructions and for other work with symmetry. Prior to having students work with a Mira (Reflecta), it is helpful to do some wax paper-folding activities: draw a line segment (or crease to form a line segment) and fold the paper to divide the line segment into two equal parts; draw any angle (or make two creases to form an angle) and fold the paper to divide the angle into two equal parts. If this brief paper-folding experience is followed by the use of a Mira (Reflecta), the students make an easy connection between the role (i.e., a flip line) and the placement of the fold in the paper and the role and the appropriate positioning of a Mira in completing the activities. Many students are fascinated by the reflecting properties of a Mira (Reflecta). For paper-folding activities, see Olson (1975).

In these activities, students investigate how to bisect a line segment and an angle; how to construct perpendicular bisectors of sides of triangles, medians, angle bisectors, and altitudes and discover their concurrencies in different triangles; and how to construct parallel lines. Discussing and questioning student results should lead students to formulate a number of different conjectures related to these constructions.

Activity 16: Slides, Flips, and Turns

Materials: Copies of Activity Sheet 16 for students; Miras (Reflectas); tracing paper; geoboards

The concepts of slides (translations), flips (reflections), and turns (rotations) are informally introduced, explored, and applied in this activity. Using Miras is helpful in working with flips, but students should have experience drawing the flips and then use a Mira to check their result. Students tend to have the most difficulty in visualizing turns; give students experience in using tracing paper to copy a figure; they can then actually turn the traced copy.

Discussing and questioning student results should lead to a consideration of what properties are preserved by slide, turn, and flip motions (e.g., shape, line segments, rays, angles, length of line segments, measure of angle, parallelism). Students should recognize that each of the three transformations is an isometry (i.e., the resulting figure is congruent to the original figure). Also, in investigating properties students should discover that orientation is not preserved under a flip. (Instances of this are seen when a slide is flipped over in a slide projector and the two projections are compared or when the reverse lettering of the word "ambulance" on the front of a vehicle is seen correctly when viewed through the rearview mirror of a car traveling in front of the ambulance.)

Transformations that distort or change a figure should be considered briefly (e.g., images in curved mirrors at amusement parks, which make the viewer look tall or short, fat or thin; a rectangle transformed by doubling one pair of sides and halving the other pair; enlargements).

In describing transformations in section 4 of this activity, students frequently give different descriptions of the same problem. Encourage students to listen to and verify the alternative solutions of their peers. In this way students realize that there need not be only one right answer to a problem.

In section 5, using a geoboard and recording the results on dot paper provide another context for exploring transformations and developing visual skills.

Extensions (section 6): Product or composite transformations are briefly presented for exploration and are designed to develop an intuitive understanding of such transformations. Only two examples of each are given (i.e., two flips in parallel lines and two flips in intersecting lines). Students are asked to make predictions (conjectures) on this limited experience. Students should be encouraged to explore additional examples to verify their conjectures. Conjectures such as the following might be proposed by students: (1) The composite motion of two flips in parallel lines is equivalent to a slide. The direction of the slide is on a line perpendicular to the parallel lines. The length of the slide is twice the distance between the parallel lines. (2) The composite motion of two flips in intersecting lines is equivalent to a turn. The measure of the angle of the turn is twice the measure of the angle between the two intersecting lines.

Activity 17: Symmetry

Materials: Copies of Activity Sheet 17 for students

There are many real-world applications of symmetry. Students should be encouraged to collect (and place in their portfolios) examples of line (reflectional), translational, and rotational symmetry. These examples might include commercial logos of banks, companies, and car manufacturers; quilt patterns; fabric and wallpaper patterns; flag designs; and art works. For ideas on symmetry in American folk art, see Zaslavsky (1990).

The four activity cards related to symmetry in this set are designed to provide specific examples of the van Hiele level of thinking as described in the Introduction. (See Fuys, Geddes, and Tischler [1988].)

Activities 18a and 18b: Exploring Symmetry with Computer Software

Materials: Logo and Geometric PreSupposer software; computers; and copies of Activity Sheets 18a and 18b for students (For other geometric investigative software, see Geometric Connectors and The Geometer's Sketchpad.)

Activity 18a teaches the REPEAT command in Logo and its use in creating patterns illustrating rotational symmetry.

Activity 18b investigates the REFLECTION (Flip) command in the Geometric PreSupposer and its use in exploring the properties of line symmetry.

Activity 19: Transformations and Coordinates

Materials: Copies of Activity Sheet 19 for students, Miras (Reflectas), tracing paper

Before doing this set of activities, students should have some experience in plotting points in the four quadrants of the coordinate plane. Students should also have completed some introductory activities on the concepts of slides, flips, and turns. Emphasis in these activities involving transformations in a coordinate plane is on pattern finding, expressing patterns in symbols, and formulating generalizations. For additional activities, see Burger (1982).

EVALUATION NOTES FOR ACTIVITIES 15–19

Reason for evaluation:

To assess students' higher-order thinking and approaches to "what if" extensions of problems

Activities 15–19

Teacher assignments for student portfolios and activities:

Complete Activity Sheets 15–19.

Complete Venn diagram on symmetry:

In the diagram below, there are eight regions and seven patterns. Each pattern goes in a separate region, depending on what type of symmetry it has. For example, a figure that has line symmetry and translational symmetry but not rotational symmetry will go in the region marked *. Indicate where each pattern goes by writing its number in the diagram. There will be one region with no, pattern assigned—can you draw a pattern that will go in this region?

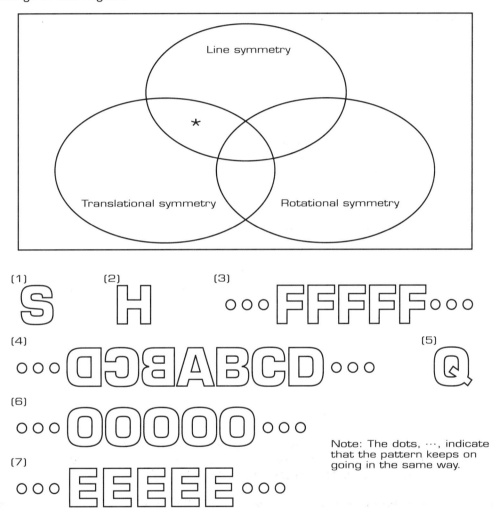

Note: The dots, ⋯, indicate that the pattern keeps on going in the same way.

Evaluation of portfolios and activities:

1. Many of the Mira (Reflecta) activities (Activity 15) are self-checking; conjectures made by students on the basis of their constructions should be reviewed for accuracy.

2. The last two activities in Activity 17 (Quadrilaterals and Symmetry, Polygons and Symmetry) and the Venn diagram on symmetry are appropriate assessment activities to determine students' higher-order thinking skills on this topic.

3. The Investigation activity at the end of sections a, b, and c of Activity 19 can serve as culminating assessment tasks to gain insight into students' approach to transformations in the coordinate plane.

ACTIVITY 15
MIRA (REFLECTA) ACTIVITIES

1. Place a Mira (Reflecta) on line *m* and read the message.

_____ *m*

HErrOi

2. Using a Mira, find the center of the circle.

3. Use a Mira to draw the perpendicular bisectors of *AB*, *CD*, and *EF*.

4. Find the *circumcenter* (the center of the circumscribed circle) for each triangle by using a Mira. (Note: This center is where the *perpendicular bisectors of the sides* of the triangle meet.)

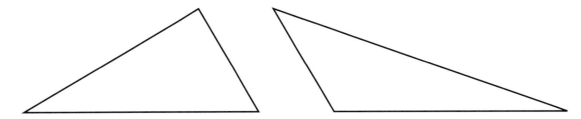

Note the position of the circumcenter in the above triangles. Why do they differ? Predict where the circumcenter of a right triangle is located. Test your prediction. What conjecture can you make about the three perpendicular bisectors of the sides of any triangle?

5. Using a Mira, construct the three medians of the triangle. (Note: A *median* of a triangle is a line from a vertex to the midpoint of the opposite side.) The point where the three medians meet is called the *centroid* or *center of gravity*.

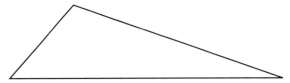

At home, cut out a cardboard triangle and find its centroid. Take a straight pin and try balancing and spinning the triangle on the tip of the pin. Success? If not, try again.

What conjecture would you make about the three medians of any triangle?

6. Use a Mira to find a position where the image of ray *OA* maps onto ray *OB*. Draw the Mira line. What does this line do to angle *AOB*?

7. Find the *incenter* (center of the inscribed circle) of each triangle, using a Mira. (Note: This center is where the three *angle bisectors* of the triangle meet.)

   What conjecture would you make about the three angle bisectors of any triangle?

8. Using a Mira, draw a line perpendicular to line *q* through point *P*. Also draw a line perpendicular to line *q* through point *S*.

9. Draw the three altitudes of the triangle, using a Mira. (Note: An *altitude* of a triangle is a line from a vertex drawn perpendicular to the opposite side.)

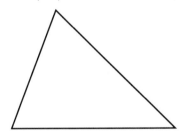

   a. Sketch an obtuse triangle *TUB* with obtuse angle at *U*. Will the altitude from *T* fall inside the triangle? Why or why not?

   b. Where will the three altitudes of a right triangle meet?

   c. What conjecture would you make about the three altitudes of any triangle?

10. Which of these lines are parallel? Check with your Mira. (Only two of the lines are parallel.)

   a _____

   b _____

   c _____

11. Draw a line through point *A* parallel to line *p*, using a Mira. Test your result for parallelism.

   ● *A*

   _____ *p*

Let's look at some illustrations involving slides, flips, and turns. In each of the following, identify the motion involved—is it a slide? A flip? A turn?

  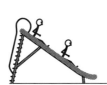  

_____ _____ _____ _____ _____

In describing a *slide* (translation), we indicate the direction of the slide by a slide arrow that connects a point to its image point. For example: Figure A' is the slide image of figure A. The slide arrow shows the direction of the slide. In this example, by using the dot paper we can say the direction is 4 to the right and 1 up; this is sometimes written as (4,1).

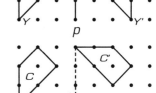

In describing a *flip* (reflection), we indicate the flip line; notice that the flip line is the perpendicular bisector of any line segment joining a point to its image. For example: Figure B' is a flip image of figure B where p is the flip line. Notice that line p is the perpendicular bisector of segment XX' or of segment YY'.

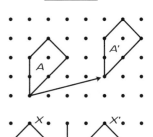

In describing a *turn* (rotation), we indicate the point of the turn, the direction of the turn, and the angle or size of the turn. For example: Figure C' is a turn image of figure C around point O. Figure C has been turned clockwise approximately 90 degrees.

1. a. Which figures are *slide* images of figure A? Indicate the slide arrow.

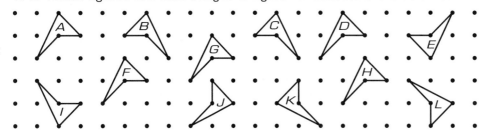

   b. Which figures are *flip* images of figure A? Find the flip lines.

2. Draw each *flip* image using the dotted line as the flip line.

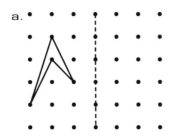   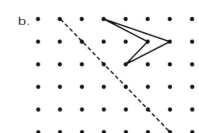

3. Turn (rotate) figure *CAT* 180 degrees around point *O*. Check your result by using tracing paper (trace *CAT* and turn the tracing paper copy to see if it fits on top of your answer).

4. Describe one motion that will map the first figure onto the second.

   a. Map figure A onto figure B.
   b. Map figure A onto figure C.
   c. Map figure B onto figure D.
   d. Map figure B onto figure E.
   e. Map figure E onto figure F.
   f. Map figure C onto figure E.
   g. Map figure A onto figure F.

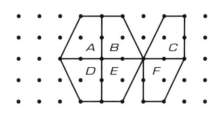

5. Motions on a Geoboard (Work with a partner, each having a geoboard.)

   a. Place a rubber band on your geoboard to use as a flip line. Form a shape on the left side of the line; have your partner create the flip image of your shape. Record results on dot paper. Repeat for another shape. Your partner does the same. What properties are preserved in this transformation? What properties are not preserved?

   b. On the lower left-hand corner of your geoboard, form a small scalene triangle. Have your partner create a slide image of this triangle using a slide arrow of (2, 3). Record on dot paper your triangle and its image. Your partner does the same. What properties are preserved in this transformation?

   c. On the center portion of your geoboard form a scalene right triangle. Have your partner create the image of this triangle by rotating it 90 degrees clockwise around the vertex of the right angle. Record results on dot paper. What properties are preserved in this transformation?

6. Extensions: Composite transformations

   a. Examine what occurs if a figure is flipped over two parallel lines—that is, flip A over line *c* to form image A′, then flip A′ over line *d* to form image A″. How is A related to A″? Is it possible to get from A to A″ in one motion? Describe.

   From these two examples, what prediction might you make about the result obtained by doing two flips in parallel lines?

   b. Repeat part a, only this time do two flips over intersecting lines.

   From these two examples, what prediction might you make about the result obtained by doing two flips in intersecting lines?

ACTIVITY 17
SYMMETRY

CUTTING SHAPES—ONE FOLD

Materials: Scrap paper, scissors

Directions: 1. Fold the paper once.
2. Cut out a piece along the fold line, and unfold it. Try to make these shapes.

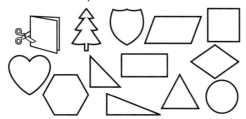

Some cannot be made!
Some can be made in more than one way.

Variation—Two Folds

1. Fold the paper twice, as shown.
2. Cut out pieces around the corner, and unfold. Try to make the shapes above. Which can be made this way? Which cannot?

COORDINATES AND SYMMETRY

Materials: Grid paper, pencil

Directions: On a piece of grid paper, draw x- and y-coordinates. Draw a line of symmetry on one of the axes, as shown. Mark some points, then mark points that correspond when reflected across the line of symmetry. Record as shown. Look for a pattern.

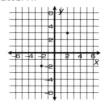 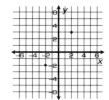

(-6, 1) -> (__, __)   (-6, 1) -> (__, __)
(0, 4) -> (__, __)   (0, 4) -> (__, __)
(2, 3) -> (__, __)   (2, 3) -> (__, __)
(4, 0) -> (__, __)   (4, 0) -> (__, __)
(-2, -2) -> (__, __)   (-2, -2) -> (__, __)

In general, if the line of symmetry is the x-axis, $(x, y) -> (\underline{}, \underline{})$.

In general, if the line of symmetry is the y-axis, $(x, y) -> (\underline{}, \underline{})$.

QUADRILATERALS AND SYMMETRY

Materials: Assorted cutout quadrilaterals, paper, pencil

Directions: Sort the quadrilaterals into these piles:

No lines of symmetry
Exactly one line of symmetry
Exactly two lines of symmetry
Exactly three lines of symmetry
Exactly four lines of symmetry
More than four lines of symmetry

1. Do any piles have *no* quadrilaterals? If so, can you draw quadrilaterals for the pile? If not, why not?
2. Look at the quadrilaterals with four lines of symmetry. What can you say about them? (For example, "They are all _____.")
3. Look at the quadrilaterals with two lines of symmetry. The lines of symmetry can pass either through vertices, or through edges. What can you say about these two types of quadrilaterals with two lines of symmetry?
4. Repeat question 3 for quadrilaterals with one line of symmetry.
5. Can a quadrilateral have *no* line symmetry but have rotational symmetry? Explain.

POLYGONS AND SYMMETRY

Materials: Paper, pencil

Directions: Try to draw polygons that fit in each space on this grid. Many cannot be done!

Number of lines of symmetry

	0	1	2	3	4	5	6
Triangle (3 sides)		△		✕			
Quadrilat'l (4 sides)			◇		✕		
Pentagon (5 sides)	⬠						
Hexagon (6 sides)							

1. For a given number of sides, can you always make a polygon with no lines of symmetry? With one? Why?

2. Can you see any patterns that would help you to predict which spaces can be filled in for seven-sided polygons?

ACTIVITY 18A
EXPLORING SYMMETRY WITH LOGO

1. Examine the following set of Logo turtle commands and sketch the turtle's path:

    FD 60   Sketch:

    RT 90

    FD 60

    RT 90

    FD 60

    RT 90

    FD 60

    RT 90

    END

    We can develop a shorthand way of writing this set of commands by using a REPEAT command to teach the turtle how to draw this shape, which we will call BOX. Examine the following procedure and then type it on the computer:

    TO BOX

    REPEAT 4 [FD 60 RT 90]

    END

    To have the turtle draw the shape, just type BOX. Explain why this gives the same result as the first set of commands.

2. Now that the turtle knows how to BOX, let's see what spectacular designs the turtle can draw. Consider the following:

    TO DAISY

    REPEAT 36 [BOX RT 10]

    END

    What do you think the turtle will draw? Describe or sketch the result.

    Now type in the procedure and then type DAISY.

    WOW! Isn't that great? Describe your result in terms of rotational symmetry.

    If the RT 10 command were changed to RT 20, what other change(s) would be needed to obtain a result that looks like the DAISY design? Explain.

3. Now it's your turn. Teach the turtle to make a shape like this sketch. Call it FLAG. Now use the REPEAT command to create a design using FLAG that illustrates rotational symmetry.

4. Design your own turtle illustration of rotational symmetry. Have fun!

ACTIVITY 18B
EXPLORING REFLECTIONS (FLIPS) WITH THE GEOMETRIC PRESUPPOSER

1. Use the Draw command and create any triangle *ABC*; use the Grid command; draw a vertical line *PQ*; reflect triangle *ABC* over line *PQ*. Is the reflected triangle congruent to triangle *ABC*? Justify your conclusion with specific evidence.

   Draw a horizontal line *MN* and reflect triangle *ABC* over line *MN*. Is the new triangle congruent to triangle *ABC*? Justify your conclusion.

   Draw a slanted line *RS* and reflect triangle *ABC* over line *RS*. Is this new triangle congruent to triangle *ABC*? Justify your conclusion.

   On the basis of these explorations, what conjecture(s) would you make concerning reflections of a triangle over a line?

2. Use the same procedure as above to investigate the following situation:

   A given figure is reflected over two parallel lines that are 3 units apart; that is, the given figure is reflected over the first line and the result is then reflected over the second line.

   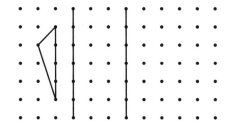

   Describe the position and the characteristics of the final figure in relation to the given figure. Note the distance between the corresponding points of the original figure and the final figure.

   Repeat the investigation with the parallel lines 4 units apart and again with the lines 6 units apart.

   How could the resulting motion of two reflections (flips) in parallel lines be described more simply?

   What conjecture can you make about the resulting motion of a figure after two reflections in parallel lines?

3. Repeat the same procedure to investigate the question of reflecting a figure over two lines that intersect at an angle of 90 degrees; repeat at an angle of 45 degrees. What conjecture can you make about the resulting motion of a figure after two reflections in intersecting lines?

   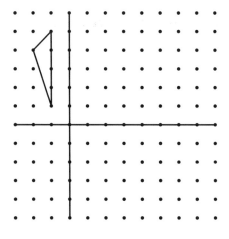

ACTIVITY 19
TRANSFORMATIONS AND COORDINATES

1. A *slide* is shown on the graph at the right. Draw the quadrilateral obtained by sliding *ABCD* as indicated by the arrow.

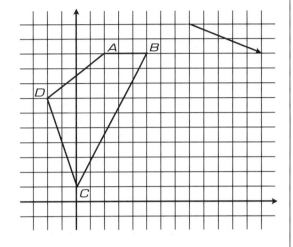

a. Label the points of the new quadrilateral so that *A*→*A'*, *B*→*B'*, and so on. Then fill in the table:

Coordinates of the original point	Coordinates of the image (after slide)
A (2, 10)	*A'*
B	*B'*
C	*C'*
D	*D'*
(Pick another one)	

b. Can you see a pattern in the numbers? Describe it in words.

c. Can you describe the pattern in symbols? (,   )→(,   )

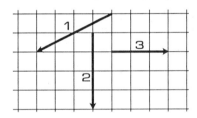

d. Investigation: Can you predict what will happen for any other slide? Use the procedure above to find rules for other slides, such as those shown at the left.

2. Try this procedure again, this time for a *flip* about a diagonal.

Draw the quadrilateral obtained by flipping *ABCD* over the dotted line.

a. Label the points of the new quadrilateral *A'B'C'D'* so that *A*→*A'*, and so on. Then fill in this table:

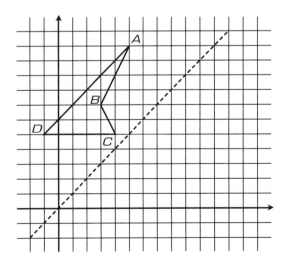

Coordinates of the original point	Coordinates of the image (after flip)
A (5, 11)	*A'*
B	*B'*
C	*C'*
D	*D'*
(Pick another one)	

b. Can you see a pattern in the numbers? Describe it in words.

c. Can you describe the pattern in symbols? (,   )→(,   )

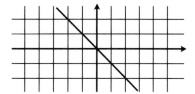

d. Investigation: Can you predict what will happen for other flips? Try the procedure above for flips around (over) the lines shown (the other diagonal and the two axes).

3. Try the procedure once more, this time for a *rotation* about the origin. Draw the quadrilateral obtained by rotating *ABCD* 90 degrees as shown at the right. (Use tracing paper.)

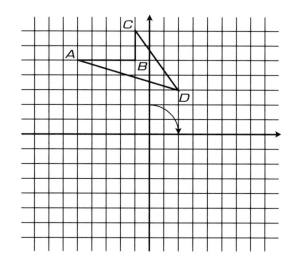

a. Label the points of the new quadrilateral *A'B'C'D'* so that *A→A'*, and so on. Then fill in this table:

Coordinates of the original point	Coordinates of the image (after turn)
A (-5, 5)	A'
B	B'
C	C'
D	D'
(Pick another one)	

b. Can you see a pattern in the numbers? Describe it in words.

c. Can you describe the pattern in symbols? (,   )→(,   )

d. Investigation: What happens for other rotations? Try it for 90 degrees counterclockwise and 180 degrees, both around the origin (point *O*).

CLUSTER D
ENRICHMENT TOPICS

Activity 20: Topology: Rubber Sheet Geometry

Activity 21: A Geometry Walk

Activity 22: Dream Vacation: A Geometry Safari

OBJECTIVES OF CLUSTER D:

1. To explore ideas related to topology—a rubber sheet geometry—and contrast them with concepts in Euclidean geometry

2. To enhance spatial visualization skills

3. To promote awareness of the uses of geometry in our environment and to examine the functions and uses of geometric shapes in real-world settings

4. To apply mathematical thinking and modeling to solve problems that arise in other disciplines, such as art, music, social studies, and science

5. To value the role of mathematics in our culture and society

6. To develop an appreciation of geometry as a means of describing the physical world

TEACHING NOTES FOR CLUSTER D:

The enrichment activities presented in this section were prepared by middle school teachers who have found geometry activities highly motivational, interesting, and challenging for their students. The activities capture the spirit of many of the features presented in the standard on geometry in the *Curriculum and Evaluation Standards for School Mathematics* (NCTM 1989).

Activity Sheet 20: Topology: Rubber Sheet Geometry (grade 7 or 8)

Materials: Rubber bands; balloons; "twisters" (for tying plastic bags); copies of Activity Sheet 20 for students

The lesson on topology starts with a problem on finding the perimeter of a rectangle to demonstrate that in Euclidean geometry, we usually think of figures in terms of congruence, measurement, similarity, and preservation of size.

Topology is introduced as rubber sheet geometry by having the students work with rubber bands and balloons (on which circles are drawn). Students, working in cooperative groups, stretch rubber bands to form squares, triangles, rectangles, and other shapes; note the topological equivalence of these figures; and recognize that the usual Euclidean properties of congruence, size, and measurement do not hold. When stretching the balloon (with a point *P* inside the circle) into different shapes, the notion of outside and inside a figure is recognized as a property of topology (namely, one cannot get from the outside to the inside of a figure without crossing the boundary). In doing the problems, students visualize better by using the "twisters" to form some of the shapes and letters.

Answers: Topologically equivalent figures as drawn on the sheet:
Example 5: a, e, k; b, i; c, d, h; f, m; g, n; j, l. Example 6: (a) C, J, I, L, M, N, S, U, V, W, Z; (b) O, D; (c) E, F, G, T, Y; (d) K, X

For homework, assign a "journal write" in which students are to describe topology and tell what they think about the lesson; also assign a "distortion-stretching" activity (on different grids) with one initial of their names. Samples of students' homework assignments are included below. Follow-up lessons include other topological concepts (e.g., mazes, Möbius strip).

Sample student "distortion" activity (fig. 23):

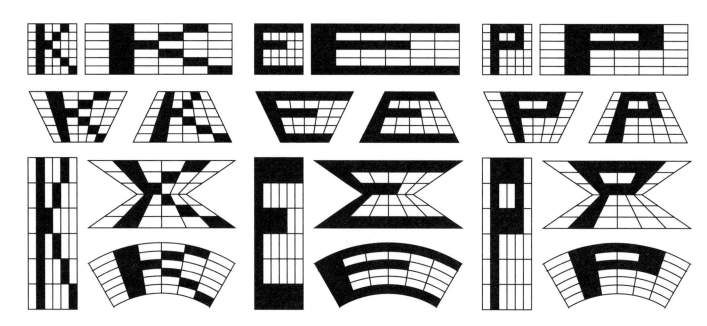

Fig. 23

Activity 21: A Geometry Walk

Materials: Copies of Activity Sheet 21 for students

As you plan this activity, explore your school building, school playground, and nearby neighborhood and note questions that will encourage students to find geometric shapes or objects and determine their use. Have students consider why many things are shaped as they are in terms of both function and aesthetics. Adapt or use with your class the Geometry Treasure Hunt idea presented with the accompanying discussion questions. For further activities, see Nelson and Leutzinger (1979).

Activity 22: Dream Vacation: A Geometry Safari (grade 6 or 7)

Materials: Art materials (construction paper, markers, scissors, tapes, and so on); brochures from travel agencies for selected countries; daily newspapers; almanacs and encyclopedias (optional videotapes: *Donald in Mathemagic Land* [Disney Productions 1987] and *Fractal Fantasy* [Fitch 1988])

This activity is designed as a cooperative learning, interdisciplinary (relating geometry to other disciplines) research project in which geometry, consumer mathematics, and logic are applied to real-life situations. Student groups of four members cooperatively plan and develop their projects—usually one period each week for fifteen weeks. In each group, students work on different aspects of the project and frequently confer with each other outside the mathematics classroom. Interim group progress reports should be given.

Since this is a "Dream Vacation," the students need to use their imaginations. It may be useful to show the videotape of Donald's imagination and fantasy in *Donald in Mathemagic Land* and the videotape *Fractal Fantasy*, which depicts an exciting and imaginative merging of art, music, science, and mathematics.

The final group projects are in the form of a visual presentation and a journal containing written explanations, analyses, and commentary on items 1–12. Students exhibit and give an oral overview presentation of their project to the class and possibly to other classes at a Math Fair.

For further examples of projects and enrichment activities, see Farrell (1988), Pollard (1985), and Trowell (1990).

EVALUATION NOTES FOR ACTIVITIES 20–22

Reasons for evaluation:

- To assess students' grasp of topological ideas
- To assess students' awareness of geometry in the real world
- To assess students' recognition of geometry in relation to other disciplines
- To stimulate creative problem solving in cooperative groups
- To encourage cooperative groups to develop a well-organized, well-designed, and imaginative presentation of a group project

Teacher assignments for student portfolios and activities:

1. Complete "journal writes" as noted in Activities 20–22.

2. Complete Activity Sheets 20 and 21.

3. Complete "A Geometry Safari" group project in Activity 22.

Evaluation of portfolios and activities:

1. Through "journal writes," monitor students' ability to reflect on their experiences and to explain the mathematical concepts involved.

2. Review completed activity sheets for accuracy and any misconceptions; note students' use of higher-order thinking in responding to questions.

3. After each group presentation, the class will assess the project on the basis of a set of standards or criteria that were established before the group projects began. The teacher will review the total project in terms of accuracy, organization, creativity, ability to give clear logical explanations, and overall presentation (visual, written, oral).

ACTIVITY 20
TOPOLOGY: RUBBER SHEET GEOMETRY

1. Explain how to find the perimeters of the figures at the right. How would you describe these figures?

2. Take a rubber band and stretch it to form different geometric shapes, such as a triangle, a rectangle, and a pentagon. Can you transform your triangle into a square? Into a trapezoid? Into a circular shape? Describe some of the figures you created.

3. Take one of the balloons that has a circle drawn on it with a point *P* inside the circle. Without breaking the balloon, try to stretch or distort the circle so it becomes a square, a rectangle, and a pentagon. Is point *P* still inside each of these figures? Describe your results.

4. In topology, or rubber sheet geometry, you may stretch or twist figures, but you may not cut or tear them. This means that two figures are topologically equivalent when stretched, if you do not disconnect two points that were connected; similarly, you cannot connect two points that were disconnected. For example:

   Figure A is topologically equivalent to figure B, but figure A is not topologically equivalent to figure C. Why?

   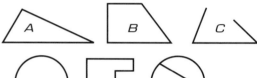

   Figure D is topologically equivalent to figure E, but figure D is not topologically equivalent to figure F. Why?

5. Which of the following figures are topologically equivalent?

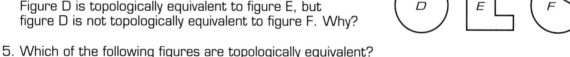

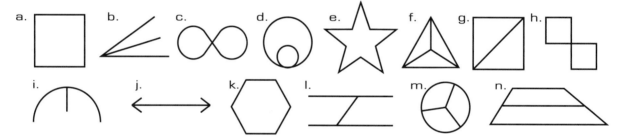

6. Consider the following set of alphabet letters:

A B C D E F G H I J K L M
N O P Q R S T U V W X Y Z

   a. Which letters are topologically equivalent to the tenth letter?

   b. Are any letters topologically equivalent to O?

   c. Which letters are topologically equivalent to E?

   d. Are any letters topologically equivalent to K?

ACTIVITY 21
A GEOMETRY WALK

1. If you saw these figures on the way to school, what special geometric name would you give to each shape?

2. Now you are going for a Geometry Treasure Hunt.

	Sketch it.	Give its location.	Describe its use.

Can you find—

an angle?

a triangle?

a pentagon?

a hexagon?

an octagon?

a circle?

a semicircle?

a trapezoid?

a cylinder?

a cone?

a sphere?

a hemisphere?

| | Sketch it. | Give its location. | Describe its use. |

Can you find—

a nonrectangular prism?

a square pyramid?

parallel lines?

perpendicular lines?

two nonparallel lines that do not intersect?

tessellations?

a line of symmetry?

congruent figures?

similar figures?

an unusual shape?

3. Discuss the following questions in your group:

   a. Why are bike wheels or skateboard wheels shaped like circles instead of squares?

   b. Why are openings in a bike rack in the shape of long narrow rectangles?

   c. Why are manhole covers circular and not square?

   d. Why are traffic signs of different shapes?

   e. What shape are the smokestacks on most factory buildings? Why do you think they are built in that shape?

   f. Why are there different shapes for buildings? Which shape building do you like best? Why?

   g. What shape rectangle is most pleasing to your eye? Sketch one. Why are index cards made in sizes 3 x 5, 4 x 6, and 6 x 8? Are these shapes pleasing to your eye? (Do some research on the Golden Rectangle.)

4. Do a "journal write": Describe your Geometric Treasure Hunt in a note to a friend.

ACTIVITY 22
DREAM VACATION: A GEOMETRY SAFARI

Here's $10 000 to plan an exciting dream vacation—a geometry safari to any country in the world where the United States dollar is not the major currency. You have a $10 000 budget to travel with three friends for three weeks (you must pay for tickets, travel, food, hotels, gifts, car rental, extras, and so on). To plan this trip, you should consider the following activities:

1. Collect brochures, maps, and literature on the chosen country and begin a scrapbook with newspaper and magazine clippings about the country: culture, history, landmarks, language, and current events.

2. Calculate the cost of the selected hotels, room service, special excursions, and so on. Prices are found in brochures and from interviews with travel agents.

3. Develop a daily itinerary, which should be mapped out on local maps. Distance is to be calculated between the countries and cities involved. Find longer distances between cities and countries on a globe—use string to create great circle arcs. Calculate distance both in standard and metric units.

4. Create a visual display (approximately 2 feet by 1 foot) of some structure or event for which the country is famous. For example, classical Greek architecture is based on rectangles and the Golden Ratio. Examine the geometric aspects of historical structures in terms of their importance in the country's culture. Other examples in other countries include the following: in Egypt, the pyramids; in Mexico, the temples, which reflect the ancient Mayan calendar; in Iran, Islamic art; in Spain, tilings and tessellations. Your display and accompanying report should depict and explain the geometric ideas involved.

5. Replicate the country's flag. Determine the scale used when comparing the replicated version to the actual flag. Discuss any types of symmetry found in the flag design.

6. Examine some of the country's stamps and currency (coin and paper) for different types of symmetry. Research the meaning and importance of certain issues.

7. Include reports of famous mathematicians, writers, scientists, artists, and explorers who have represented that particular country.

8. Examine the country's arts and crafts and architecture. Describe and give examples of geometric designs—do certain shapes predominate in their work?

9. Choose one of the country's folk songs and describe any examples of transformations (slides, flips, or turns) that you find in the music. For example, here are four bars of music showing the use of motion geometry:

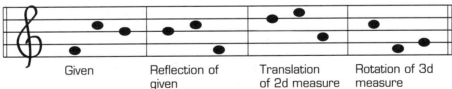

| Given | Reflection of given | Translation of 2d measure | Rotation of 3d measure |

   As an alternative activity, create your own tune (using motion geometry) inspired by the country.

10. Research the country's topography, such as mountains or deserts, including rainfall and climate. Think of fractals and how the landscapes are depicted.

11. Write daily entries in a journal describing your adventures, thoughts, feelings, and questions.

12. You are to solve any problem that may disrupt your travel plans. For example, what happens if your funds are depleted (due to possible inflation in the country) and you can't afford the hotel rates? Report how such problems were solved and discuss alternative solutions.

◆   ◆   ◆   ◆   ◆   ◆   ◆   ◆

REFERENCES

Apostol, Tom. *The Theorem of Pythagoras*. Reston, Va.: National Council of Teachers of Mathematics, 1988. (Videotape and guide)

Artzt, Alice F., and Claire M. Newman. *How to Use Cooperative Learning in the Mathematics Class*. Reston, Va.: National Council of Teachers of Mathematics, 1990.

Baroody, Arthur J. "One Point of View: Manipulatives Don't Come with Guarantees." *Arithmetic Teacher* 37 (October 1989): 4–5.

Battista, Michael, and Douglas H. Clements. "Constructing Geometric Concepts in Logo." *Arithmetic Teacher* 38 (November 1990): 15–17.

Bazik, Edna F. "Tangrams." In *Projects to Enrich School Mathematics, Level 2,* edited by Leroy Sachs, pp. 42–47. Reston, Va.: National Council of Teachers of Mathematics, 1988.

Bezuszka, Stanley, Margaret Kenney, and Linda Silvey. *Tessellations: The Geometry of Patterns*. Palo Alto, Calif.: Creative Publications, 1977.

Bezuk, Nadine. *Understanding Rational Numbers and Proportions*. Reston, Va.: National Council of Teachers of Mathematics, forthcoming.

Burger, William F. "Graph Paper Geometry." In *Mathematics for the Middle Grades (5–9)*. 1982 Yearbook of the National Council of Teachers of Mathematics, edited by Linda Silvey, pp. 102–17. Reston, Va.: The Council, 1982.

Chazen, Daniel, and Richard Houde. *How to Use Conjecturing and Microcomputers to Teach Geometry*. Reston, Va.: National Council of Teachers of Mathematics, 1989.

Crowley, Mary. "The van Hiele Model of the Development of Geometric Thought." In *Learning and Teaching Geometry, K–12*. 1987 Yearbook of the National Council of Teachers of Mathematics, edited by Mary M. Lindquist, pp. 1–16. Reston, Va.: The Council, 1987.

Davidson, Neil, ed. *Cooperative Learning in Mathematics*. Menlo Park, Calif.: Addison-Wesley Publishing Co., 1989.

Del Grande, John. *Geometry and Spatial Sense*. Reston, Va.: National Council of Teachers of Mathematics, forthcoming.

Disney Productions. *Donald in Mathemagic Land*. Los Angeles, Calif.: Disney Productions, 1987. (Videotape)

Engelhardt, John, compiler. *Geometry in Our World*. Reston, Va.: National Council of Teachers of Mathematics, 1987.

Farrell, Margaret A., ed. *Imaginative Ideas for the Teacher of Mathematics, Grades K–12: Ranucci's Reservoir*. Reston, Va.: National Council of Teachers of Mathematics, 1988.

Fitch, Charles. *Fractal Fantasy*. Mill Valley, Calif.: Media Magic, 1988. (Videotape)

Freudenthal, Hans. *Mathematics As an Educational Task*. Dordrecht, The Netherlands: D. Reidel, 1973.

Fuys, David, Dorothy Geddes, and Rosamond Tischler. *The van Hiele Model of Thinking in Geometry among Adolescents. Journal for Research in Mathematics Education* Monograph No. 3. Reston, Va.: National Council of Teachers of Mathematics, 1988.

Geddes, Dorothy. *Measurement in the Middle Grades*. Reston, Va.: National Council of Teachers of Mathematics, forthcoming.

Giganti, Paul, Jr., and Mary Jo Citadino. "The Art of Tessellation." *Arithmetic Teacher* 37 (March 1990): 6–16.

Hill, Jane M., ed. *Geometry for Grades K–6*. Reston, Va.: National Council of Teachers of Mathematics, 1987.

Hilton, Peter, and Jean Pedersen. *Build Your Own Polyhedra*. Menlo Park, Calif.: Addison-Wesley Publishing Co., 1988.

Hirsch, Christian R., and Glenda Lappan. "Transition to High School Mathematics." *Mathematics Teacher* 82 (November 1989): 614–18.

Kenney, Margaret, and Stanley Bezuszka. *Tessellations Using LOGO*. Palo Alto, Calif.: Dale Seymour Publications, 1989.

Kroll, Diana Lambdin, and Frank K. Lester, Jr. "Appendix 1: Evaluation." In *Developing Number Sense in the Middle Grades*, by Barbara Reys, pp. 50–54. Reston, Va.: National Council of Teachers of Mathematics, 1991.

Lappan, Glenda, and Mary Jean Winter. "Spatial Visualization." In *Mathematics for the Middle Grades (5–9)*. 1982 Yearbook of the National Council of Teachers of Mathematics, edited by Linda Silvey, pp. 118–29. Reston, Va.: The Council, 1982.

Maletsky, Evan M., ed. *Teaching with Student Math Notes*. Reston, Va.: National Council of Teachers of Mathematics, 1987.

Mathematics Resource Project. *Geometry and Spatial Visualization*. Palo Alto, Calif.: Creative Publications, 1978.

Moore, Margaret L. *LOGO Discoveries*. Palo Alto, Calif.: Creative Publications, 1984.

National Council of Supervisors of Mathematics. "Essential Mathematics for the Twenty-first Century." *Mathematics Teacher* 82 (September 1989): 470–74.

National Council of Teachers of Mathematics. *An Agenda for Action*. Reston, Va.: The Council, 1980.

_____. *Arithmetic Teacher* 37 (February 1990). Focus Issue: Spatial Sense.

_____. *Curriculum and Evaluation Standards for School Mathematics*. Reston, Va.: The Council, 1989.

_____. Curriculum and Evaluation Standards for School Mathematics Addenda Series, Grades K–6, edited by Miriam A. Leiva. Reston, Va.: The Council, 1991–92.

_____. Curriculum and Evaluation Standards for School Mathematics Addenda Series, Grades 5–8, edited by Frances R. Curcio. Reston, Va.: The Council, 1991–92.

_____. Curriculum and Evaluation Standards for School Mathematics Addenda Series, Grades 9–12, edited by Christian R. Hirsch. Reston, Va.: The Council, 1991–92.

_____. *Learning and Teaching Geometry, K–12*. 1987 Yearbook of the National Council of Teachers of Mathematics, edited by Mary Montgomery Lindquist. Reston, Va.: The Council, 1987.

_____. *Mathematics Teacher* 78 (September 1985). Special Issue: Geometry.

_____. *Professional Standards for Teaching Mathematics*. Reston, Va.: The Council, 1991.

National Research Council. *Everybody Counts*. Washington, D.C.: National Academy Press, 1989.

Nelson, Glenn, and Larry P. Leutzinger. "Let's Take a Geometry Walk." *Arithmetic Teacher* 27 (November 1979): 2–4.

Niess, Martin. "LOGO Learning Tools Build Informal Geometry Ideas." *Computing Teacher* 15 (November 1988): 11–15.

O'Daffer, Phares G., and Stanley R. Clemens. *Geometry: An Investigative Approach*, 2d Ed. Reading, Mass.: Addison-Wesley Publishing Co., 1992.

Olson, Alton T. *Mathematics through Paper Folding*. Reston, Va.: National Council of Teachers of Mathematics, 1975.

Onslow, Barry. "Pentominoes Revisited." *Arithmetic Teacher* 37 (May 1990): 5–9.

Phillips, Elizabeth. *Patterns and Functions.* Reston, Va.: National Council of Teachers of Mathematics, 1991.

Pohl, Victoria. *How to Enrich Geometry Using String Designs.* Reston, Va.: National Council of Teachers of Mathematics, 1986.

Pollard, Jeanne. *Building Toothpick Bridges.* Palo Alto, Calif.: Dale Seymour Publications, 1985.

Reys, Barbara. *Developing Number Sense in the Middle Grades.* Reston, Va.: National Council of Teachers of Mathematics, 1991.

Rowan, Thomas. "Report of the Task Force on Addenda to the NCTM K–12 *Curriculum and Evaluation Standards for School Mathematics.*" Reston, Va.: National Council of Teachers of Mathematics. Unpublished report, November 1988.

Serra, Michael. *Discovering Geometry.* Berkeley, Calif.: Key Curriculum Press, 1989.

Shaughnessy, J. Michael, and William F. Burger. "Spadework Prior to Deduction in Geometry." *Mathematics Teacher* 78 (September 1985): 419–28.

Steen, Lynn Arthur. "Teaching Mathematics for Tomorrow's World." *Educational Leadership* 47 (September 1989):18–22.

Trowell, Judith M., ed. *Projects to Enrich School Mathematics: Level 1.* Reston, Va.: National Council of Teachers of Mathematics, 1990.

van Hiele, Pierre M. "A Child's Thought and Geometry." In English translation of selected writings of Dina van Heile-Geldof and P. M. van Hiele, edited by David Fuys, Dorothy Geddes, and Rosamond Tischler, pp. 243–52. Brooklyn: Brooklyn College, 1984. (Original document in French. La Pensée de l'enfant et la géométrie, *Bulletin de l'Association des Professeurs de Mathématiques de l'Enseignment Public,* 1959, 198, 199–205.)

van Hiele-Geldof, Dina. "The Didactics of Geometry in the Lowest Class of Secondary School." In English translation of selected writings of Dina van Heile-Geldof and P. M. van Hiele, edited by David Fuys, Dorothy Geddes, and Rosamond Tischler, pp. 1–214. Brooklyn: Brooklyn College, 1984. (Original document in Dutch. De didaktiek van de meetkunde in de eerste klas van het V. H. M. O., Unpublished doctoral dissertation, University of Utrecht, 1957).

Vygotsky, Lev. *Thought and Language.* Cambridge, Mass.: MIT Press, 1934/1986.

Walter, Marion I. *Boxes, Squares, and Other Things.* Reston, Va.: National Council of Teachers of Mathematics, 1970.

Wilmot, Barbara. "Creative Problem Solving and Red Yarn." *Arithmetic Teacher* 33 (December 1985): 3–5.

Winter, Mary Jean, Glenda Lappan, Elizabeth Phillips, and William Fitzgerald. *Spatial Visualization.* Middle Grades Mathematics Project. Menlo Park, Calif.: Addison-Wesley Publishing Co., 1986.

Zaslavsky, Claudia. "Symmetry in American Folk Art." *Arithmetic Teacher* 38 (September 1990): 6–12.

Zawojewski, Judith. *Dealing with Data and Chance.* Reston, Va.: National Council of Teachers of Mathematics, 1991.

COMPUTER SOFTWARE

Companies producing different versions of Logo software:

Logo Computer Systems, Inc., 330 West 58th Street, Suite 5M, New York, NY 10019

Terrapin, 400 Riverside Street, Portland, ME 04103

Geometric investigation software:

Geometric PreSupposer. Sunburst Communications, 101 Castleton Street, Pleasantville, NY 10570

Geometric Supposer. Sunburst Communications

Geometric Connectors. Sunburst Communications

Elastic Lines. Sunburst Communications

The Geometer's Sketchpad. Key Curriculum Press, 2512 Martin Luther King, Jr., Way, P. O. Box 2304, Berkeley, CA 94702

Database software:

AppleWorks. Apple Computer, 20525 Mariani Avenue, Cupertino, CA 95014

MECC Create-A-Base. MECC, 3490 Lexington Avenue North, Saint Paul, MN 55112

Activity 2a: Building polyhedra
Cut out the patterns for the polyhedra; fold the patterns
along the dotted lines and carefully tape edges to form solids.

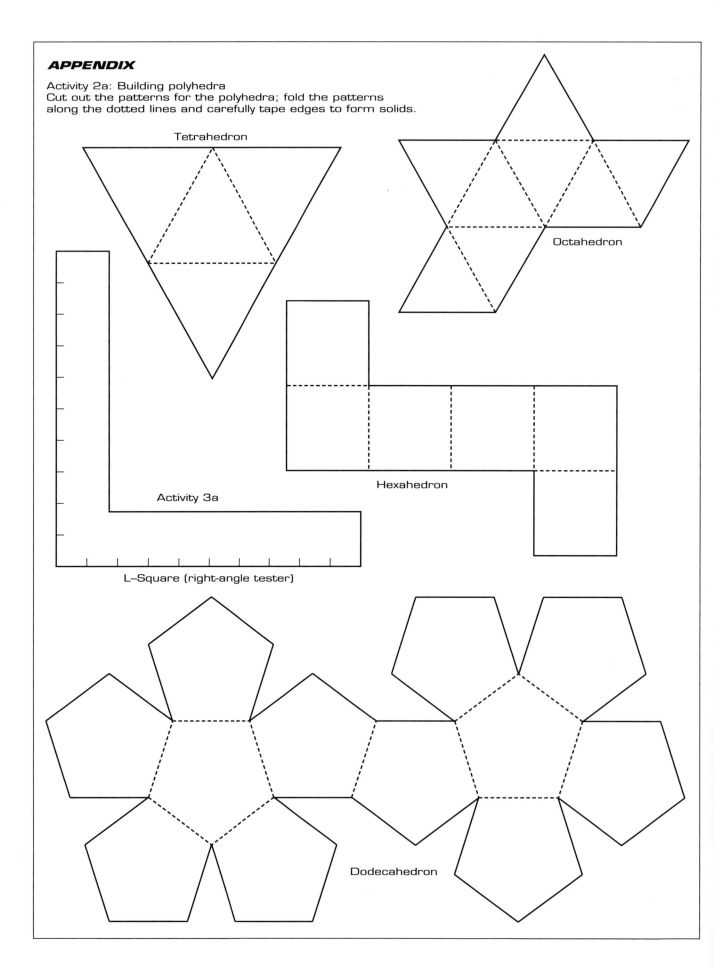

Tetrahedron

Octahedron

Activity 3a

Hexahedron

L–Square (right-angle tester)

Dodecahedron

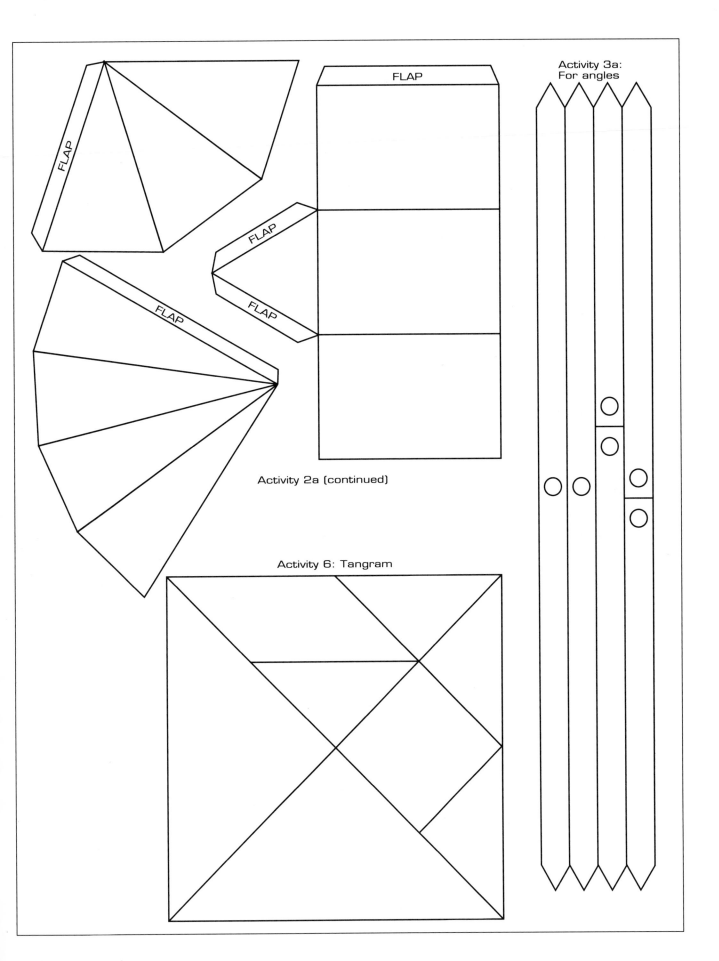

FLAP

FLAP

FLAP

FLAP

FLAP

Activity 2a (continued)

Activity 3a:
For angles

Activity 6: Tangram

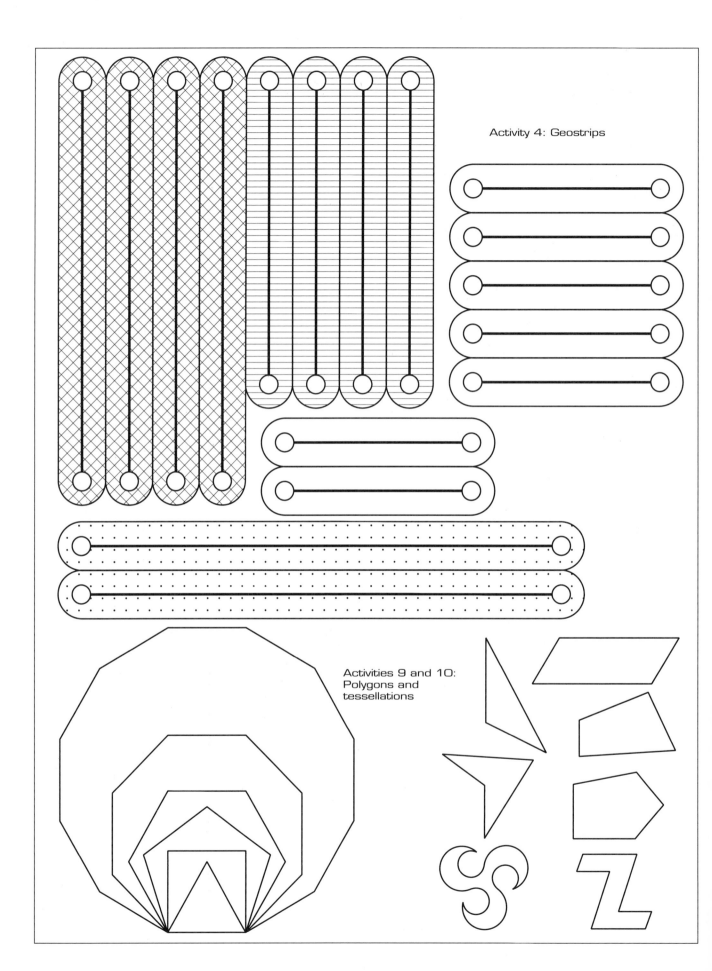

Activity 4: Geostrips

Activities 9 and 10:
Polygons and
tessellations